Universal Evolution

LOUIS JACOT

Universal Evolution

(translated from the French by Gwenda Stephens)

ÉDITIONS DU MONT-BLANC

TABLE OF CONTENTS

TABLE OF PLATES

FOREWORD

Science has developed to such an extent in modern times that it is no longer possible to grasp a picture of it as a whole. The fact that certain scientific findings are mathematically incontestable yet contradictory does not help the situation. By widening its field of activity through increasingly improved analysis, science has accumulated a mass of information, accurate but incomplete, voluminous but disconnected. This analysis, which is in effect a kind of "dismantling" of the Universe, can only develop by concentrating more and more on detail. The final result is that so many dissected parts are spread out for consideration that it is impossible to distinguish the essential from the minor detail.

But scientific methods are not confined to analysis and are only of value if the "dismantling" operation is followed by a "remounting" of all the separate parts into the complete mechanism of the Universe. To be valid, this operation must be based on a knowledge of the proper place of each part and of its function in the structure as a whole. This presupposes a certain conception of the way in which the entire system works, or at any rate admits of theories on the subject being put forward and checked.

A useful purpose would be served if the results of these various analyses were to be fitted into a broad picture ranging from the infinitely large to the infinitesimally small and covering not only astronomy, geology and physics but also the phenomena of life and thought. This book is accordingly designed to give form to this loose mass of disconnected information, evaluate once again the shades of importance between the essential and the minor factor, and throw into relief the fundamental phenomenon controlling all existence, a knowledge of which is indispensable to all who want to understand the world in which they live—universal evolution.

CHAPTER I

PROOF OF UNIVERSAL EVOLUTION

1. Motions and shapes of galaxies

Photographs of nebulae such as the Great Nebula of Andromeda, the M 51 and NGC 4736 of the Hunting Dogs and the M 101 of the Big Bear (see Plate 1) are not only instructive but amazing when it is considered that all stars are grouped into various clusters of this kind, called galaxies. The sun is part of a galaxy—none other than that of the Milky Way.

The first impression given by these photographs is one of general motion. This is particularly noticeable in the spiral nebulae whose vortex drive cannot be doubted. The fact that galaxies are spread out over tremendous distances gives an idea of the fantastic motion actuating these clusters.

The second impression conveyed by these photographs is of unstableness in the galactic systems. The spiral formations, in particular, show motion starting from the centre and extending progressively towards the exterior through the effect of centrifugal force. Everything in the vortex is thrust further and further away from the nucleus and there is no possibility of any return to the centre of the spiral. This change of shape is therefore irreversible, the second form assumed by a galaxy through the effect of vortex motion automatically excluding any return to its original shape.

The motion of nebulae can be compared to Catherine Wheel fireworks which throw off sparks of light while rotating around a central axis.

At the galactic scale, there are vast systems driven by motions giving them variable shapes. As these changes of shape are irreversible, continuous evolution of the Universe can be observed at this level.

But these variable forms are not the only signs of galactic evolution. The distances between the centres of the galaxies also change (by increase) through the ages. This phenomenon is well known; it is based on a principle similar to that which governs sound waves. According to this principle, a motor-car horn becomes higher pitched as the vehicle approaches, and lower pitched as it moves away. The behaviour of light waves is similar to that of sound waves. If a source of light moves at high speed in relation to an observer—or rather, to a spectrograph that breaks down light—the spectral lines characteristic of certain bodies do not occupy the same positions in relation to the colours of the spectrum as when the light source is immobile. The lines move towards red when the light source withdraws and towards violet when it approaches. This is known as the Doppler-Fizeau effect. Now, in the nebulae spectra, the lines shift towards red, thus indicating that the galaxies are moving away. The American astronomer, Hubble, of Mount Wilson Observatory, enunciating the theory that has now been given his name, established that the velocity of withdrawal of the galaxies increases in proportion to their distance from observer. It is approximately 160 kilometres a second per million light years. While certain nebulae fairly close to our galaxy are withdrawing at a speed of 500 km/sec, those furthest removed but still visible from the Earth are moving away at a velocity in excess of 100,000 km/sec.

This withdrawal of the galaxies, implying as it does an increase in the diameter (that is, an expansion) of what is commonly called the Universe, warrants consideration. Although at first glance this phenomenon seems to upset all preconceived ideas of the permanence of the Universe, it is actually an irrevocable consequence of universal motion which, by its very definition, excludes all permanence. This question will be dealt with in greater detail in the following chapter. It is enough for the moment to note that the expansion of the Universe is an irrefutable proof of its evolution.

2. Solar activity

Passing from the galactic scale to that of the heavenly bodies included in these vast systems, it will be seen that the sun is far from being an inert mass. Astronomers have calculated that it moves through the heart of the galaxy at the speed of approximately 200 km/sec, that it rotates on its own axis about once every 25 days, and finally that it is the seat of intense activity. This is demonstrated by the spots and solar eruptions that accompany magnetic storms. Prominences as high as 900,000 kilometres—that is, greater than the sun's radius (see Plate 2)—have been photographed. Solar activity assumes proportions beyond anything imaginable.

Although it is known that the sun lights the Earth, there is generally very little interest shown in the cause of this phenomenon, and yet a modicum of thought would make it clear that solar radiation implies release of energy and loss of mass—in other words, continuous evolution of the sun.

This affects not only the sun itself but all stars similarly diffusing light rays through space. Radiation sometimes assumes considerable proportions, celestial bodies known as "novae" or "supernovae" momentarily giving off extraordinary bursts of light.

Like the galaxies to which they belong, stars are subject to continuous evolution. This will be studied in greater detail in Chapter Five.

3. Evolution of planets and comets

Our planet, the Earth, has not always had the same appearance that it has today. Its shore-lines have been modified continuously

through the ages. Its climates have undergone very wide variations : at certain periods, immense areas that now have temperate
climates were covered with a layer of ice a thousand metres thick ;
at others, tropical vegetation extended right up to the polar circles.
Seas were completely dried up, as vast salt and gypsum deposits
indicate. Mountain ranges were formed through the ages and
then considerably reduced by erosion. Some have disappeared
altogether from the Earth's relief and geologists have only been
able to establish their existence by stratigraphic studies of ground
upheavals. Erosion is not a phenomenon of the past ; even now,
millions of tons of material are being swept daily from the continents into the seas. Volcanic eruptions occur at different points
of the globe. In short, the evolutionary process is taking place
continuously and visibly.

Nor do the other planets escape this general process (see
Plate 3) which, as will also be seen later (Chapter Five), constitutes
the fundamental principle governing their existence.

Evolution is much more spectacular in the case of the comets
than in that of the planets (see Plate 4). Their enormous tails,
sometimes extending over several million kilometres, indicate
rapid disintegration of the celestial body. Photographs of comet
tails taken on several successive nights show them breaking up and
being scattered through space. Comets not only supply proof
that the celestial bodies are far from being as solid and compact
as is generally supposed, but also reveal the most complex mysteries
of evolution (Chapter Five, Section 6).

4. *Evolution of matter*

Leaving the world of celestial bodies for the infinitesimal world
in the heart of matter, certain striking phenomena—the expansive
force of gases, electricity, magnetism, chemical reactions, etc.—
indicate that so-called inert matter is capable of moving, and

violently, even to the point of explosion. Admittedly, these movements are not necessarily proof of evolution. This is particularly true of certain reversible-chemical reactions, for example, in which associations can be followed by dissociations returning the bodies in question to their previous state. Nevertheless, evolution is implied in all motion, as will be seen later.

One of the most spectacular and unchallengeable demonstrations of the evolution of matter is radioactivity. This consists of a continuous transformation of so-called radioactive elements— uranium, radium, thorium, polonium, etc.—into a simpler element, lead, by the emission of alpha, beta and gamma particles. In this case, the process is not only irreversible to the extent that it is not possible to reunite the elements resulting from fission, but unavoidable as it is impossible to prevent radium atoms from being radioactive, that is from emitting elements and transforming themselves into lead atoms (see Plate 5).

Radioactivity is of capital importance for an understanding of evolution. It not only shows that the process extends from the infinitely large to the infinitesimally small, but makes it clear that—everything in the Universe being interdependent—macrocosmic evolution can only be the result of microcosmic evolution, and vice-versa, and that the cause of universal evolution is the same everywhere. This matter will be more fully discussed in subsequent chapters.

5. *Evolution of life*

If there is one context in which the process of evolution cannot be denied it is that of life. Pluricellular beings are unquestionably born, grow old and die. They are never the same for two days in succession. Their life is an evolution, more or less rapid according to type, from birth to death.

Unicellular beings that reproduce themselves by simple cellular division also evolve. Admittedly certain varieties have remained unchanged through the ages, but the individual that escapes death by dividing into two continues, not as a permanent entity, but in the form of two separate beings, different from each other and different from the one from which they sprang; these, in turn, if they do not die by accident, form four separate beings, then eight, etc. In other words, all living things are subject to the evolutionary process.

When it comes to species, the process is equally manifest. Paleontologists have succeded in reconstituting not only the flora but also the fauna that existed during the different geological periods of the Primary, Secondary, Tertiary and Quaternary eras and again, whether in the main groups of plants, fish (hard shelled, cartilaginous, bony), batracians, reptiles or vertebrata, the process is everywhere to be seen (see Plate 6). It was very late in the history of the Earth, in the Cretaceous period at the end of the Secondary era, that flowering plants appeared. Up to that time, vegetation on our planet was quite different from anything known today.

The Quaternary era was introduced by paleontologists merely to mark the appearance on Earth of Man, the latest arrival in the evolution of the species, but in fact it differs very little from the Tertiary.

6. Evolution of thought

The mind of the individual is intimately linked with the life and development of the brain. Cerebral evolution is observable in the evolution of the species and it is precisely Man's extraordinary mental development that distinguishes him from other beings (see Plate 6).

The fundamental idea dominating the creation of all beings from earliest times to the present day is the preservation of life by adaptation to changes in condition due to evolution of the Earth. But even though this elemental drive persists, the thought process, as far as the means used to achieve this end are concerned, has undeniably developed.

If the subject is now narrowed down to human thought, evolution will be observed as much in the scientific and religious fields as in the philosophic—in the latter case, particularly from the sociological standpoint. Humanity has erected the thought process on the foundations of ancient knowledge that is constantly being revised. Intellectual development does not, of course, advance continuously in the way normally understood by the word "progress", which is synonymous with improvement; everything depends on Man's conditions of life at any given period, and on the trials he has to face. However, there has definitely been an evolution in Man's conception of human society since he first appeared on Earth.

7. Proof

The foregoing is proof that evolution exists and is a general and universal phenomenon, ranging simultaneously from the infinitely large (galaxies) to the infinitesimally small (elements comprising matter) and from the purely physical field (radioactivity) to the complex phenomena of life and thought.

The universality of evolution is of profound significance.

CHAPTER II

PROFOUND SIGNIFICANCE OF EVOLUTION

1. Definition of evolution

Evolution is change. It is not, however, just any kind of change. This term is normally not applied to fortuitous changes or to chaotic movements brought about by various exterior causes. According to the etymology of the verb "evolve", meaning unroll, the word evolution should imply continuous development, produced by an unvarying cause.

2. Cause of evolution

As evolution is change, it must be the result of motion, and cannot be conceived of in any other context. The primary cause of evolution is therefore motion. This statement may at first appear oversimplified, but is actually of the utmost importance. It places the evolutionary process in its true context and obliges us to make the necessary distinction between evolution and fortuitous movement.

3. What is motion?

This will seem a trivial question. Everyone knows perfectly well what motion is. Unfortunately questions are not often raised in the presence of familiar phenomena, their mere repetition appearing to be an explanation in itself. The same applies to motion. A certain number of ways of producing motion having been devised, investigations are rarely carried further. And yet motion actually merits particular study as it is the cause of all phenomena and conceals the enigmas of life.

A full exposition of this engrossing subject has already been given [1] and will not be repeated here. To understand what follows it will be sufficient to summarize the essentials.

4. Motion and immobility

A body is generally considered to be in motion when it changes its position in relation to the others surrounding it, and to be immobile when it does not so change. Motion is thus defined as the change of place of one body in relation to its environment. Now this is an arbitrary simplification of reality, only one movement being taken into account, the others disregarded. If a table is said to be immobile merely because its position remains the same in relation to the other objects in the room then, deliberately or unconsciously, due consideration is not being given to the fact that the table is actually moving with the Earth, not only on its own axis but also around the sun at the rate of 30 km/sec. The movements of the particles that constitute the table are also being disregarded. It is in fact absurd to decide whether an object is stationary or mobile merely on the basis of the slowest of all the movements that actuate it.

Similarly, it is illogical to consider moving objects as being immobile merely because their respective positions are not modified. Soldiers marching forward in rank are not stationary, although their respective positions remain the same. This error in wording obscures the very nature of motion. To understand it, a closer

---

[1] *Méditations sur le mouvement*, by Louis JACOT, Editions du Scorpion, Paris.

study should be made of two of its aspects—overall motion and inner movements—that are usually treated most casually.

5. *Overall motion*

Particles can be actuated by movements that are either random or coordinated. In the former case (an explosion, for example), they are scattered in different directions; in the latter (a moving train or the Earth travelling through space), they are all carried along in the same direction. The two categories differ only in the direction of displacement. It is obviously not reasonable to consider the particles in the first instance as moving and in the second as being at rest or inert. All are in motion. If various objects placed on a table retain their respective positions, it is not because they are inert or immobile but because they are all actuated by the same overall translation of the Earth through space at the rate of 30 km/sec. Inertia is therefore not, as is generally supposed, the opposite of motion but the dynamic resultant of various motions. This distinction is particularly important. The erroneous idea that inertia is synonymous with absence of movement is at the root of the most serious scientific misunderstandings.

Overall motions can be superimposed at various levels or incorporated one in the other. For example, the movement of a train (or of the moon) occurs in the context of the Earth's motion around the sun which, in its turn, is taking part in the general motion of the galaxy to which it belongs, and finally, of the galaxies which are all moving away from each other.

6. *Inner movements*

Turning from the macrocosmic to the microcosmic, it will be seen that within each atom all the particles of which it is composed are in motion. Emphasis must be placed on the word "all".

There is not a single particle that will ever be found to be resting. (See Chapter Seven.) This may seem surprising at first, but as the entire Universe is in motion and at no point settled, how could the particles of the Universe be immobile?

Movement inside matter indicates not only that matter and movement are indissolubly bound, but that matter without movement does not exist.

To put it another way, the intrinsic nature of matter is motion. There is not a single grain of inert, elementary dust capable of moving or stopping itself. Elementary particles are formed essentially by movement. This point must be emphasized as it is of capital importance. The Universe does not contain matter plus motion but motion that assumes certain aspects known as matter. The resistance of bodies, for example, is not due to inertia (which is non-existent) but to the movements of their constituent particles. The shape of bodies is also the result of various movements. For example, they change shape if they are heated or cooled, that is if the movement of their constituent particles is modified. In short, there is no property in matter that is not the result of the movement of its constituent particles. Motion is therefore literally the very essence of matter.

It will be said in opposition that something that moves cannot be nothing and that if it is not nothing it is necessarily matter. This argument leads back to the error of dissociating matter from motion and of assuming that one can exist without the other. Instead of trying to understand the exact nature of matter, it is automatically and unconsciously assumed that matter is the basis of everything that exists.

Obviously it is not possible for nothing to move, but if all the properties of a particle are due to movement, then it is not logical to ascribe to the particle the additional feature of existing outside its own movement. It is as erroneous to say that the Universe contains a substance other than movement as to assert that a lake is one thing and the water of which it is composed another. Just

as a lake is inseparable from water, matter cannot be separated
from motion because matter and motion are one and the same
thing. Anyone not convinced of this should try to identify a property in matter that is not the result of motion.

7. *The dynamic Universe*

A particle that moves inevitably brings pressure to bear on
those surrounding it. It therefore constitutes a force. The
concept of force is inseparable from that of motion. No force can
exert itself otherwise than by motion; similarly motion cannot be
other than force.

As the elementary particles of the Universe are composed of
movement, they are forces. This means that the entire Universe,
as much in its overall structure as in its separate parts, is of a
dynamic nature. On this basis, it is possible to understand the
ultimate significance of Einstein's famous formula: $e = mc^2$ in
which e represents energy, m mass and c^2 the square of the velocity
of light. As this velocity can be considered constant in a given
case, Einstein's formula, by posing mass-energy equivalence,
clearly indicates that the intrinsic nature of matter is motion.
Unless physics are based on this fact they are nothing but fiction.

As force is required to move an object, it is unconsciously
considered to be outside the object. But force cannot be outside
everything otherwise it would be produced by nothing, which is
inadmissible. Force cannot be outside the constituent particles of
the Universe. On the contrary, being the result of their movement,
it is closely associated with them. In other words, where there is
a particle, there is motion (and force); conversely, where there is
motion (and force) there is a particle. This fundamental truth
must be constantly borne in mind and will be raised again later.

Accordingly motion is not, as is commonly assumed, a purely
passing phenomenon capable of affecting or not affecting certain

objects; neither is it a simple change of position; motion pene-
trates and actuates all bodies to the point of constituting the
absolute essence of the Universe.

Movement cannot be stored up in the form of rest or immobility,
as might be supposed from the fact that it is possible to move
certain physical objects at will. In such cases, as will be seen
later (Chapter Seven, Section 3), only the direction of movement
changes; movement itself cannot do other than move, just as
force must exert pressure and is unable to avoid so exerting.

As force cannot avoid exerting pressure, and as pressure is
always a transmission of force, that is a transmission of motion,
the various particles of the Universe, through contact, are constantly in the process of transmitting motion (cf. Chapter Four,
Section 1). The particle with more movement transmits its surplus to its neighbour (like two gear wheels) in such a way that
their movements, while still being movements, cancel each other
out. No particle has a movement separate from that of the
others. All are simultaneously active and passive participants in
universal motion. All are interdependent (see Plate 7).

This equalization of motion is responsible for all phenomena,
whether the shifting of objects or of light, electricity, heat, etc.
As movement is transmitted from particle to particle, everything
in the Universe is interdependent, evolution in the infinitesimally
small affecting the infinitely large, and vice versa.

8. *Profound significance of evolution*

Briefly, the first conclusion to be drawn from evolution observed
at the various levels of the Universe (galaxies, stars, planets, atoms)
is that motion is the very essence of universal matter. This means
that matter and motion are indissolubly bound, that matter
without motion does not exist, and that motion, which actuates
all bodies, is not constituted by a mere shift of position.

The second conclusion is that as every particle is movement, every particle is a force. Therefore, by its very nature the Universe is dynamic.

The third conclusion is that as motion transmits itself from particle to particle, it is impossible for one part of the Universe (and of matter) to be permanent and another to be evolving. The evolutionary process is generalized and affects all particles. If some particular particles appear to be stable, that is merely because the period during which they are under observation is too short. As just pointed out, it is because of this transmission of movement from particle to particle that everything in the Universe is interdependent and that evolution in the infinitely large is the result of that in the infinitesimally small and vice-versa. By studying the movement inside the elementary particle, the evolutionary process at the various levels of the Universe will be understood. This will be done in the following chapter.

Finally, the fourth conclusion is that as matter is movement, everything in the Universe that strikes the senses and is assumed to be fact is actually nothing but phenomenon—matter as much as light. (This too will be referred to again, later.)

CHAPTER III

MAIN FEATURES AND BROAD OUTLINES
OF EVOLUTION

1. Unit of matter

Every moving particle is a force and all forces that move amongst other forces exert on them a pressure that is reciprocal, each force simultaneously being exerted upon and exerting. Endured pressure is normally called resistance, but is actually the same as applied pressure, resistance being nothing but pressure in the reverse direction.

A moving force that meets a resistance is limited by it. This limitation gives it shape. The shape of bodies is the result of the cancelling out of various movements in contact, the unit with more movement transmitting its surplus to those with less. As the shapes of bodies are the result of movement, they are never permanent.

This equalization of movements in contact is very important as, by limiting forces and giving them shape, it makes units of them, all with the same amount of movement. Without the creation of such units, no organized world could be built up and the Universe, if it existed at all, would be completely chaotic.

Force that meets equal pressure on all sides assumes a spherical form. As all the forces of the Universe are in contact one with the other and continuously in the process of equalizing their motions, the sphere is the inevitable plastic resultant of all elementary particles (see Plate 7) and responsible for the fact that they are units. They are not independent, of course, as their movements are constantly being equalized, but they constitute units nevertheless since they are actuated by an internal motion of their own. Now to see what that motion is.

2. *Motion inside a unit of matter*

A surprising thing is immediately noticed. It is not possible for the movement inside the sphere to be "spherical". Even if it were to start from the centre and radiate uniformly towards the surface, the resistance it would encounter there would oblige it, as motion never stops, to continue its path inside (Chapter Two, Section 7; Chapter Seven, Section 3). In short, as movement inside the sphere cannot be spherical, it becomes circular.

Circular motion shifting in a circular direction does not oppose itself but, on the contrary, benefits from its own pressure which catches up with it from behind in such a way that it actuates itself. In a sense, circular motion is therefore the "natural" movement inside a sphere.

The dynamic resultant of internal movement therefore does not tally with the spherical form (that is, the plastic resultant) produced by the equalization of movements between particle and particle. This discrepancy between the plastic resultant of opposing forces, that is the sphere, and the dynamic resultant, i.e., the movement of rotation inside the sphere, is the cause of evolution. In fact the inequality between the external pressure sustained by a particle because of its neighbours and the pressure exerted by its own internal movement results in the sphere progressively losing its shape, becoming flattened at the poles and swollen at the equator (see Plate 7).

The distortion of a rotating sphere can readily be illustrated by laboratory experiment.

The result of the discrepancy between the plastic and dynamic resultants and of the inequality between the pressures and resistances exerted and sustained by the elementary particles is that all the particles of the Universe progressively lose their shape: they become flattened at the poles and swollen at the equator.

The salient feature of universal evolution is therefore general expansion of universal matter.

As the diameter of particles increases through the ages, the density of universal matter decreases.

3. Evolution in reverse

The next thing to consider is whether expansion is without limit. Since its roots are to be found in the deformation of the spherical mass in rotation, it necessarily will come to an end when the rotary movement ceases. But a rotary movement cannot continue indefinitely as such precisely because of this process of deformation. In other words, when the speed of a given circular movement decreases beyond a certain point it triggers off a movement in the reverse direction. This phenomenon can be observed, for example, in the Catherine Wheel fireworks which, having thrown off sparks while rotating in one direction, suddenly start to turn in the other. This change in the direction of rotation has been put to advantage by the manufacturers of toys such as the "yo-yo". The latter, which consists of a grooved disc around which a string is wound, assumes a regular movement in a descending direction as the string unwinds, then automatically throws itself into reverse and ascends as the string rewinds.

This reversal-of-rotation phenomenon is easily understood when the deformation of a rotary movement is studied. Inevitably a point is reached at which the "circular" movement, by dint of extending progressively in an outward direction, is finally thrown into reverse.

4. Pulsating Universe

There is therefore every reason to assume that the elementary particles of the Universe pass through successive phases in which they unwind (by expanding) and rewind (by contracting) and that these phases affect the Universe as much in its overall structure as in each of its separate parts.

The period of expansion (the present) is characterized by an increase in the volume of all the particles of the Universe. Thrusting against each other, they are responsible for an increase in the diameter of all bodies and consequently of those vast systems or groups of stars known as galaxies. This expansion of the nebulae gives the impression that they are "speeding away". In fact, the galaxies are not speeding away at all as they actually remain in contact with each other through their constituent particles. However, in view of this common expansion, their centres necessarily move further apart. This progressive increase in the distance between the centres (the only visible parts) gives the impression that they are speeding away and it is this phenomenon which has been named "the Doppler-Fizeau effect" by the astronomers.

This expansion of particles is at the root of numerous phenomena that will be studied in more detail in the following chapters. It manifests itself by a continuous decrease in the density of all bodies forming the Universe to the point at which, becoming increasingly attenuated, they cease to form distinct groups and merge into an immense, indistinguishable mass. It is at this point that the rotary movement goes into reverse.

In the period of contraction following that of expansion, the particles, through reciprocal pressure, form immense groups actuated by overall movements, the intrinsic nature of particles being movement. Exerting pressure on each other, these immense systems are generally driven in a vortex form. At the centre, pressure is considerably greater than at the periphery. In a sphere, for example, concentric pressure increases from the periphery towards the centre in proportion to the decrease in the surface encountered. Accordingly, through the effect of this great pressure, the particles in the centre of these systems cohere into atoms and form material bodies.

The period of contraction comes to an end when the circular motion, straining increasingly towards the interior of the particle, produces, at the centre, a pressure greater than the peripheral resistance.   At that point, centripetal contraction is replaced by centrifugal expansion.

This change in the direction of rotation affects not only elementary particles but also galactic vortexes that lose their shape through the effect of rotation, becoming flattened at the poles and swollen at the equator.   During expansion, they expel stars, as will be seen below.

The idea of a pulsating Universe—that is, a succession of cycles during which matter is formed (bodies becoming distinguishable) and then broken down again (bodies returning to indeterminate universal substance)—is not new.   It was propounded by the Brahmins thousands of years ago.   It is in fact the only explanation that adequately accounts for the general and undeniable phenomenon of evolution and for the continuity of the Universe.   All other theories raise insurmountable problems.

CHAPTER IV

STRUCTURE AND EVOLUTION OF THE UNIVERSE

1. The Universe: vacuum or plenum?

Early in a study of the Universe, a choice has to be made between two fundamentally different and incompatible ideas: the first, that the Universe is a vacuum, the second, that it is filled.

The former springs more naturally to mind when the sun, moon and stars are observed. The Universe appears to be made up of a multitude of material (celestial) bodies between which there is nothing but empty space. This seems to be confirmed by the scientific fact that the atmosphere surrounding the Earth becomes increasingly rarefied with distance from the surface of the globe. The logical conclusion is that beyond a certain altitude, vacuum is reached. As the Earth seems always to move in the same orbit around the sun, Newton concluded that it was attracted by the sun. He accordingly postulated his famous law of "universal gravitation" according to which all bodies attract one another directly in proportion to their masses and inversely as the square of their distances. As gravitation seemed to be confirmed by certain calculations applied to the moon's orbit around the Earth, it was accepted as being responsible for the "fall" of bodies to the surface of the Earth and for the cohesion that prevented the celestial bodies from disintegrating in spite of their dizzy race through space. (The Earth, for example, moves around the sun at the rate of 30 km/sec.) Official celestial mechanics are based entirely on this theory.

The second way of explaining the Universe is through a study of the behaviour of forces. The more these are observed, the more the conclusion is reached that "the Universe hates a vacuum", to use an expression popular in antiquity. In other words, all force has a tendency to spread towards the point of least resistance. A vacuum is consequently a physical impossibility. What appears to be a vacuum is in fact full, but its density is too attenuated to be perceptible to the senses and to normal methods of investigation. It does not require much reflection, however, to realize that the Universe is not a vacuum. For example, light comes from the sun and the stars in the form of a wave the length of which has now been accurately calculated for each of its various colours. Obviously, if the space between the celestial bodies and the Earth moves in waves, it cannot be empty for the simple reason that a vacuum cannot undulate. In short, various phenomena lead the objective observer to regard inter-stellar and inter-galactic space as being full. That is what Descartes believed when he wrote in his treatise on light : "As there is no vacuum in the Universe..." His theory on vortexes was founded on this concept.

If this concept was later abandoned in favour of Newton's theory, it was due to the fact that various events, such as Le Verrier's discovery of Neptune, seemed to provide incontrovertible evidence of the accuracy of Newton's law. Le Verrier's discovery made a considerable impression because of the manner in which it was presented. Basing himself on the idea that the perturbations noted in Uranus' path were caused by the "gravitational" force of an as yet unknown planet, Le Verrier began to study these perturbations and, on the basis of Newton's law, calculated the position in which the celestial body in question should be found. He wrote finally to Hall, the Berlin astronomer, gave him the position, and asked him to study the sky in order to see if he could locate the planet. Hall discovered that it was, in fact, at the point indicated. The news of this discovery, disseminated all over Europe, had very wide repercussions. The press made much of the power of human thought which, on the basis of the purest theory and a few observations, had managed to discover new celestial bodies. This was a tribute simultaneously to Man's achievement, Le Verrier's genius and the accuracy of Newton's theory.

After a certain time, however, astronomers began to realize that the distance and the path given by Le Verrier were not accurate. The discrepancies were, in fact, enormous. Le Verrier, basing himself on Bode's law with its factor-2 geometric progression, had calculated Neptune's distance from the sun as being approximately 6,000 million kilometres whereas its mean distance is actually 4,500 million. This considerably modified the duration of its revolution around the sun according to Kepler's laws. The differences were such that Le Verrier's demonstration was no longer convincing. Nevertheless, Newton's theory, as a result, passed into the realm of certainty and his "law" continued to govern the entire field of celestial mechanics. Now, although the factors on which Le Verrier based his theories were incorrect, it was not possible to suppose that the correct result was simply due to chance. On closer study of this case, it is surprising to find that the Director of the Paris Observatory should have been obliged to ask a Berlin astronomer to study a very precise sector of the heavens in order to see if a planet was located there. The accuracy with which Le Verrier indicated the position of that planet is even more surprising. The data at his disposal enabled him to arrive at a certain number of assumptions concerning mass, distance, etc., but none of these assumptions (and they varied considerably) gave him the scientific basis for establishing such an accurate position. The discrepancies discovered later in the path of the real planet as compared to that of the supposed one are proof enough. It can therefore be assumed that Le Verrier, having discovered Neptune by means of a telescope and having had the idea that it was the cause of the perturbations noted in Uranus' path, wished to check his assumption by means of calculations and, to this end, "rigged" his demonstration.   Nothing more was needed for Newton's law to become the credo of official astronomers.

Nevertheless, a critical examination of numerous facts makes it impossible for an objective observer to support the theory of universal gravitation.   As already mentioned, the transmission of light presupposes the existence of a medium capable of rippling, that is, a dynamic medium, between the celestial bodies and the Earth.   Now, if gravitation existed, this medium would necessarily slow down the motion of the celestial bodies, in other words, would reduce their velocity.   This, however, is not the case. Comets' tails are, on the contrary, thrust away from the sun, thus indicating that there is, in the heart of the solar system, a centrifugal force (called by astronomers "radiation pressure").   This is the exact contrary of gravitation.   The law's basic assumption is that the sun "captures" celestial bodies coming from the exterior but, as will be seen later, the evolution that governs the Universe (the solar system as much as any other) is characterized by the opposite phenomenon, that is, by the expansion and dispersion of elements through centrifugal force in the stellar and galactic systems. Gravitation has never been proved.   To pretend that it is momentary is to place it outside time.   This is tantamount to admitting that it doesn't exist.   The power of attraction of a celestial body, which is proportional to the mass, can only be the sum of the power of attraction of its constituent parts.   But physicists have never been able to find, at the root of matter, any particle with power to attract in all cases.   On the contrary, they have discovered positive and negative elements whose main characteristic it is to either repel their own kind or attract their opposites.   The combination of positive and negative elements thus produces a neutral mass.   Consequently, as there is no such thing as an elementary particle with a general power of attraction, then a zero figure of attraction multiplied by any imaginable number of particles will still result in zero.   A study of the behaviour of forces, in all aspects of practical life, shows that these forces, and consequently the elementary particles, react on each other by pressure (expansion force of gases, etc.).   As to the fall of bodies, this in no way implies the existence of a power of attraction drawing them towards the "centre of the Earth", but is the natural result of the concentric pressure exerted on the celestial bodies by the surrounding medium.

Nor does Newton's law explain the individual distances of the planets from the sun according to Bode's law (Chapter Five, Section 4) or the differences in the rotation of the various planets and in the lengths of the years (tropical, sidereal, anomalistic) (Chapter Six, Section 11).   But all phenomena in the Universe are due to a sequence of causes and effects.   If, therefore, one theory is unable to explain them, another must be found.   Actually, increasing study of Newton's law leads to the conclusion that its main defect resides in the fact that it is founded on the idea of a permanent Universe, whereas it is more and more evident that the Universe is in the process of evolving.   Newton's law tried to explain why the Earth always seemed to follow the same path around the sun.   This basic assumption will be seen to be false. Hubble's law on the expansion of the Universe, which is beyond dispute, is completely incompatible with Newton's law.   If the galaxies, which constitute fantastic formations, were to attract each other directly in proportion to their masses and inversely as the square of their distances, they would not be speeding away, as the Doppler-Fiseau effect indicates, because even if their masses were to decrease, their inverse ratios would remain proportional. In short, Hubble's law excludes Newton's and is only valid in the context of a Universe that is a plenum.   A study of inter-stellar spaces on the spectrograph confirms the theory of the plenum since such spaces shift at the same time as the celestial bodies they contain.   Photographs of spiral nebulae supply convincing proof that these bodies, moving like the sun in the heart of such unstable systems, cannot follow closed orbits, as claimed by Newton's law.

The subject of Newton's law has already been fully expounded [1]. It will not be possible to give more time to it here.

2. The large vortexes

The fundamental fact that the Universe is made up of dynamic particles, whose intrinsic nature is motion and whose chief feature is expansion until resistance equal to pressure is encountered, leads necessarily to the conclusion that the Universe is a plenum.

In such a Universe, the reciprocal pressure shocks of particles in motion and in contact naturally produce two kinds of phenomena: the first is the oscillation of the particles, which is characteristic of undulatory phenomena, such as light; the second is the overall motion, generally in a spiral form, in which a very large number of particles are swept along in the same direction. The latter is explained by the fact that when a particle transmits its surplus movement to its neighbour, it necessarily affects the direction of that neighbour's movement. The neighbour, in its turn, transmits the surplus received to, and affects the direction of, the next particle. In increasing numbers, the particles are finally all thrust in the same direction. This is the well-known principle of the avalanche. It is enough that a small amount of snow be set in motion for the movement to be communicated by degrees to the mass and eventually lead to enormous quantities being swept in the same direction.

This is how mutually resisting overall motions are created in the Universe. Their reciprocal resistance limits their drive, giving them, more often than not, the form of a vortex. This is due

---

[1] *Méditations sur le mouvement*, Editions du Scorpion, Paris, *Eléments de physique évolutive*, Editions du Scorpion, Paris, *La Terre s'en va*, Editions de la Table Ronde, Paris, *L'Univers en marche*, Nouvelles Editions Latines, Paris, *Attraction ou distraction universelle ?*, Nouvelles Editions Latines, Paris, and *Idées Nouvelles sur l'Univers, la Terre, fille du Soleil*, Messeiller, Neuchâtel, Switzerland, by Louis JACOT.

partly to the fact that a movement, encountering resistance on all sides, is obliged to adopt a circular direction and partly because of the progressive expansion of all the particles. Expansion is thus marked by an increase in the diameter of the system and by the overall spiral form.

The existence of such vortexes is no longer a matter of conjecture, as was the case at the time of Descartes. Photographs of innumerable spiral nebulae supply irrefutable proof of their presence in the Universe (see Plate 1). These changeable formations unquestionably indicate that the Universe is a plenum and in the process of evolving. It cannot therefore be governed by Newton's law, which presupposes that it is a vacuum.

It goes without saying that the celestial bodies inside these large overall motions are carried along by the ambient medium and do not travel through empty space by their own energy or under the influence of an initial impulse.

The fact that the visible centres of these galactic vortexes appear very remote from each other should not lead to the erroneous supposition that they constitute the entire galaxy and that if nothing else is visible, nothing else exists. The atmosphere surrounding the Earth is also often invisible, but its existence would not be denied today.

Nebulae can be compared to spheres flattened by their motion, as indicated by numerous photographs in which the galaxies are seen, in profile, to have the shape of enormous lenses. Now, in a sphere subjected to concentric pressure (it must not be forgotten that the various systems exert pressure on each other from all sides), the pressure increases as the centre is approached because the surface on which it is exerted is progressively diminishing. Consequently, the particles comprising these systems are not all of the same size but enlarge progressively as pressure decreases, that is, from the centre towards the periphery. In other words, the further removed from the centre of the vortex, the less dense the particles. It is not surprising that their presence escapes attention

and can only be observed indirectly, by means of certain phenomena, such as the transmission of light waves.

The spiral motion is not a peculiarity of galaxies. On the
contrary, it is a general phenomenon, produced by overall motions
that can occur at various levels. Certain addenda should therefore be appended to Descartes' vortex theory, according to which
all the vortexes are to be found in the same plane. In reality,
one frequently sees them not only in juxtaposition, but also intermingled. For example, the solar system, with its planets, forms
a vortex in the heart of the galaxy (the Milky Way), while the
planets, with their satellites, form smaller vortexes in the heart of
the solar system. This subject will be dealt with in more detail in
Chapter Five.

3. Ether and matter

There are at the moment most serious misunderstandings
between scientists on the subject of ether. The majority deny its
existence. However, as certain phenomena, such as the transmission of light, magnetism, etc., can only be explained by the
presence of a transmitting medium, the euphemism "properties of
space" is adopted in order to avoid recognizing a fact that would
deal a fatal blow to certain theories. In short, misunderstanding
is deliberately fostered, leading in turn to others. What is the
explanation of this attitude?

Discussions on the subject of ether go back as far as earliest
antiquity. Anaximander of Miletus, in the Sixth Century B. C.,
considered ether the primary universal matter and defined it as
being a unique and infinite substance, capable of motion. This
theory was not accepted by all, other philosophers considering
either water, air, fire or even atoms as the basis of everything.
Then when the undulatory nature of light was demonstrated, it
seemed that the existence of ether would have to be unanimously
recognized even though this was extremely embarrassing to the

supporters of universal gravitation as, in the context of their theory, the presence of such a medium would necessarily slow down the celestial bodies and brake their motions, and this had never been observed. Subsequently certain phenomena were noted that could only be explained if a corpuscular nature were attributed to light— for example, the emission of electrons from a metallic plate on which a light beam of very short wave length had been trained. This gave rise to doubts regarding the rippling nature of light. Finally, Michelson's famous tests were carried out and dealt a decisive blow to the theory of ether.

As the Earth moves on its orbit at the rate of 30 km/sec, Michelson thought that a light ray propagated in the same direction as the Earth's translation would have a velocity of 300,030 km/sec (300,000 representing the velocity of light plus 30 for the velocity of the Earth on its orbit) whereas a ray propagated in a perpendicular direction would only have a velocity of 300,000 (merely that of light). He thought he could demonstrate the Earth's motion through space by the interferences that these light rays, actuated by different velocities and reflected on an interferometer by a system of mirrors, were expected to produce. However, the interferences did not occur. In order to explain this apparently absurd negative phenomenon that seemed to demonstrate that $300,000 + 30 = 300,000$ instead of 300,030, Einstein launched his famous theory of relativity. Following this test, which showed clearly that the Earth was not moving at the rate of 30 km/sec in relation to the surrounding ether, the majority of scientists, as they could not deny the existence of wave phenomena, began to question the existence of ether and speak of the properties of space.

This conclusion is clearly illogical. It would be inconceivable to claim that there could be sea waves without sea. Waves cannot occur without something that ripples, therefore that exists.

The correct conclusion that should have been drawn from Michelson's test was not that ether did not exist but that the preconceived idea of ether needed to be revised.

This revision would have been unnecessary if scientists had remembered Anaximander's definition, particularly in so far as it concerned ether's essential quality of being "capable of motion". A particle capable of movement is by its nature dynamic because a purely passive movement is unthinkable. Any moving mass— a billiard ball, for example—becomes a force and consequently a dynamic unit when it encounters another.

Ether is therefore not, as is commonly supposed, an inert mass that fills the Universe and through which the stars move rather like cars travelling through fog; it is dynamic and its vortex motion sweeps the stars along, in particular the Earth around the sun. Our planet therefore travels on its orbit *with* the ambient medium. In such circumstances, it was not possible for Michelson's test to demonstrate the Earth's motion at the rate of 30 km/sec in relation to its environment. The Earth is in the same situation as a traveller in a moving train: his position changes in relation to objects situated outside the train but remains unaltered inside the carriage. The premises of Michelson's test were accordingly erroneous and the expected interferences were destined never to occur. The theory of relativity is consequently constructed on a non-existent base and ether is an incontestable fact as long as it not assumed to have properties it does not possess, such as immobility and passivity.

As soon as an exact idea of the elementary particle of the Universe is acquired, that is, when its dynamic nature is recognized, the apparent contradiction between matter and ether disappears. The tendency to consider matter as the basis of everything that exists leads, first, to the presence of ether being denied because it is immaterial, then, once its existence has become patent, to "material" and "immaterial" being regarded as two entities with necessarily different natures. However, as soon as ether and matter are accepted as having the same nature, that is motion, all contradiction between material and immaterial disappears. Not only is it necessary to admit that the one exists as much as the other but also that they are closely linked, material elements being transformed into immaterial ones, as in the case of radiation phenomena, and vice versa (for example, the absorption of solar heat by matter).

But then, why are certain elements material and others immaterial, and how can these two types of particle coexist? A glance at the Universe will show that material clusters occupy the centres of vortexes, and this is precisely the explanation of the difference between material and immaterial particles. Those near the centre are subjected to much greater concentric pressure than those at the periphery. Consequently, their volume is smaller, their density proportionally greater and their internal movement faster. Offering greater resistance to light rays, they become opaque and appear to be of a different nature to the medium through which they move. In fact, they are nothing of the kind. All particles of the Universe are the same as they are of the same nature (motion) and only differ in their volume (according to the difference in the pressures to which they are subjected) and in the direction of their internal movements. The same applies to the material particles to which physicists have given different names (electrons, protons, etc.). Their position in the heart of the atom and the direction of their internal movements constitute the only differences between them (Chapter Seven).

It may appear strange at first that material elements should have the same nature as immaterial, but the distinction normally made between them is purely arbitrary. Anything of a density too attenuated to be measured by conventional scales which, being material, are unsuitable for weighing the immaterial, is simply disregarded. But it must be recognized that the vortexes of the Universe are vast unities existing at various levels. Whether galactic, solar or planetary, each vortex forms a whole and there is no valid reason to attribute to its centre a nature different from that of the peripheral areas. On the contrary, everything indicates (this point will be raised again when the evolution of the Universe at different scales is studied) that all the particles of the Universe are of the same nature—motion—and that matter is in fact nothing else but compressed ether. As soon as this basic truth is grasped, the coexistence of material and immaterial elements becomes quite understandable.

4. Creation and evolution

For a long time it was assumed that the Universe had been created at a given moment from nothing, had not altered since and would remain unaltered until the day of its destruction.

The idea of permanency is based primarily on the belief that matter is eternal and the rhythm of the years perpetual—as appears to be demonstrated by so-called universal gravitation. The assumption that the Earth is made up of everlasting material elements and always follows the same orbit around the sun naturally leads to the conclusion that it will always be thus and that the Universe is consequently permanent.

However, the numerous phenomena listed in Chapter One—speeding away of the galaxies, radiation of the stars, succession of different geological periods, radioactivity, evolution of the species, etc.—no longer permit this comfortable idea of permanency to be indulged in. From the infinitely large to the infinitesimally small, evolution is visible. The idea of it has even become familiar as these various phenomena are now widely known, but its ultimate significance has yet to be understood.

As matter appears to be immutable and as certain phenomena imply evolution, a distinction is naturally made between the permanent and the changing world. Two incompatible concepts are accordingly assumed to be valid. As all the particles of the Universe are of the same dynamic nature, it is not possible for some groups to be permanent and others changing. All are in the process of evolving in the same way, the only difference being the appearance of this process, certain masses being more stable than others according to the way in which the particles are grouped. As a result, evolution does not produce sufficiently spectacular effects at the human level to be noticeable, but this should not be allowed to be misleading. Permanency is an erroneous idea. It excludes the sequence in events and is in contradiction to the elementary fact that the present is the result of the past and that the future will be the outcome of the present. In short, it is not substantiated by experience. The writer has elsewhere [1] sought to demonstrate the incompatibility between the concepts of permanency and evolution and to contribute towards the radical change in thinking required if the idea of evolution is to be accepted. Evolution is in fact universal. It is the result of the very nature of universal matter, which is motion. Affecting all particles, it cannot be confined to certain places and certain objects. It is all-pervading and only a half-thinker could conceive of partial evolution.

5. Hubble's law

The main law of universal evolution is that enunciated by Hubble and his colleague, Humason, according to which the galaxies are speeding away at a velocity proportional to their distance from the Earth, this velocity being approximately 160 km/sec per million light years.

Hubble's law does not of course mean that the Earth is the centre of the Universe and that all the galaxies are withdrawing from it at velocities that increase as they approach the periphery. Observations are always relative to the point at which they are made. It is therefore reasonable to admit that the galaxies, which are scattered fairly equally throughout the Universe, are all expanding to more or less the same extent and thrust each other away equally. Consequently, to an observer situated in one of

[1] *Eléments de physique évolutive*, by Louis Jacot, Editions du Scorpion, Paris.

these galaxies, the furthest removed must necessarily appear to be withdrawing at a velocity proportional to the distance that separates it from him.

Hubble's law is of capital importance not only for astronomers but for all scientists and philosophers as it obliges them to raise again and reconsider all the general problems of the Universe.

The concept of an expanding Universe, that appears absurd to the mind obsessed by the idea of inert matter and permanency, becomes perfectly admissible once the relationship between matter and motion is studied, as the speeding away of the galaxies is clearly the inevitable consequence of the dynamic nature of elementary particles.

This speeding away, on the contrary, is absolutely inexplicable if, as in the case of the Newtonians, it is assumed that the Universe is a vacuum and that it is merely the distances across this void between the nebulae that increase.   Indeed, as Zwicky most pertinently stated, it is incompatible with Newton's law because if the masses remain the same, the distances between them should also remain the same.   If certain masses diminish more than others, the larger galaxies should attract them and consequently they should be in the process of approaching—and this is contrary to fact.   Even if all the galaxies were to lose a proportional part of their mass—and this is impossible as the energy radiated by a galaxy, due to mass-energy equivalence, is absorbed by the others and never lost—the inverse ratios of gravitation would not change as they are proportional to the mass.   As to the quite preposterous theory that the nebulae situated in the "centre" of the Universe lose a part of their mass, which would have to be fantastic, to the advantage of those at the periphery, this is not even in conformity with Newton's law as in such conditions the speeding away of the galaxies would be progressive and not proportional to the distances. In short, no plausible theory can reconcile Newton's and Hubble's laws.   This is not surprising as the former attempted to explain the permanence of the Universe—in particular the reason why the

Earth followed, or so it was thought, the same orbit around the sun—whereas the latter emphasizes continuous evolution, in other words, the exact contrary of permanency.

It is a pity that the scientific and philosophic significance of Hubble's law has not been better expounded over the last few years. Even a scientist as eminent as Zwicky was not led by his observations to its inevitable and logical conclusion but stopped halfway by declaring that Newton's law did not apply between the galaxies. Clearly gravitation proportional to the mass must be either universal or non-existent. The fact that it doesn't apply to the galaxies is proof that it is pure fiction. What occurs at a higher level can only be the consequence of what is occurring at lower scales. A whole is always the sum of its constituent parts. If the Universe is in the process of expanding, this is not taking place at one level only but throughout its entire structure, each of its constituent particles being involved in this expansion.

Hubble's law is therefore of the utmost importance as it unquestionably establishes :

(1) that the Universe as a whole is in the process of expanding ;
(2) that this expansion is taking place in all its parts and in each of its particles ;
(3) that the Universe is a plenum and that the expansion of its particles, transmitted from one to the other, is producing the expansion of the galaxies ;
(4) that as all the galaxies are in contact with each other, their expansion causes the distances between their visible centres to increase, thus giving the impression that they are speeding away whereas in fact there is no increase in the empty spaces between the galaxies but general expansion of the latter ;
(5) that as all the galaxies are expanding, the stellar systems (including the solar system) of which they are comprised are participating in this expansion ;

(6) that expansion of the particle is caused by its internal movement;

(7) that universal matter is the same everywhere, its intrinsic nature being motion. This is moreover demonstrated by Einstein's formula $e = mc^2$ which establishes mass-energy equivalence, e being the energy, m the mass and c^2 the square of the velocity of light. (The philosophical significance of this formula is still a long way from having been satisfactorily clarified.)

Hubble's law is therefore highly instructive as it supplies invaluable information not only on the structure of the Universe but on evolution and its causes.

EVOLUTION OF CELESTIAL BODIES

1. Expansion and radiation

The phenomena occurring in the Universe should be interpreted in the context of a deep conviction that the celestial bodies are incorporated in an evolving and expanding galaxy.

By bearing constantly in mind that the solar system is a stellar system as much as any other and equally subject to universal evolution, an acceptable explanation can also be given for the positions and motions of the celestial bodies which it contains.

All other concepts have been invalidated by the discoveries of recent years · and are based on outmoded notions of the superiority of Man and of the planet privileged by his presence.

Furthermore, when studying the solar system, the sun, planets, satellites and comets should not be considered independently of the medium in which they are found. They are not surrounded by a vacuum but are part of the overall motion of the environment in which they are carried along. (The special case of comets will be dealt with later in more detail.)

A study of the sun should therefore not be limited to the luminous globe itself but should include the medium in which it is placed, that is, the centre of a vortex which stretches beyond the known planets.

The first phenomenon to be examined is that of solar radiation. In this connection, there is nothing new in the statement that the sun radiates light and heat across space as far as the Earth. It is equally well known that astronomers have long observed intense activity in the sun, as indicated by spots, eruptions and prominences reaching as much as 900,000 kilometres in height. What is the cause of this activity? As the sun seems to be an immense clear-glowing fire, combustion is the first explanation. But combustion consists of oxydation, a chemical phenomenon affecting the peripheral elements of the atom and accordingly of very short duration. As the radiation of the sun and of the other stars is continuous, the cause must lie deeper.

The explanation is supplied by the facts that have just been noted in connection with universal evolution. As the galaxies expand, their stellar vortexes expand as well—the entire Universe being interdependent—and the celestial bodies in the centre of the vortexes consequently participate in this expansion. Their most complex material elements explode—this constitutes the phenomenon of radioactivity (cf. Chapter Seven, Section 3)—and this breaking up of bodies creates an output of energy and heat that is transmitted over great distances and produces well-known luminous phenomena as well as frequent magnetic storms. Solar radiation is, in fact, the most spectacular demonstration of the expansion of the Universe. It would be inconceivable in a permanent world, as all radiation implies evolution of matter. The inadmissible habit of combining the two incompatible principles of evolution and permanency makes it difficult to arrive at the conclusions about solar radiation that command recognition. As it is not possible for part of the Universe to be in the process of evolving and another part to be stable, solar radiation constitutes the most blinding proof of the evolution of the Universe in general and of the solar system in particular—a blinding proof that should open all eyes!

2. Rotation as such

When studying the phenomena that occur on the surface of the sun, particularly solar spots, astronomers noticed that the star rotated on its own axis in approximately 25 days.

There is a reason for every phenomenon and this applies as much to the rotation of the celestial bodies as to their translation. Now, if the theory of gravitation seemed for a while to explain certain trajectories (through the complaisance of astronomers, who attributed to the celestial bodies the masses required to enable them to satisfy the requirements of the law), it was never able to supply the least explanation of rotation. In fact, it is in contradiction to it. If gravitation existed, then a mass should influence another according to a certain mechanism and a powerful celestial body, close at hand, turning on its own axis, should produce a synchronous rotation in its neighbour. But this is definitely not the case. (This point will be raised again in the following section, in connection with the planets.) The rotation of the celestial bodies is not governed at all by so-called gravitation. The reason is simple. Rotation is the result of the overall vortex motion of which the body forms a part. The medium in which it moves carries it along and causes it to rotate. And vice versa as, in an overall motion, all particles affect each other by their movements.

Rotation is therefore the result of contact and can only be explained if the celestial bodies are studied in their naturel setting, which is the vortex.

As the solar system is an immense vortex, the sun in the centre is naturally actuated by a movement of rotation. In addition, the vortex effect extends out to the borders of the system, sweeping along with it the planets surrounding the central star. It is therefore the cause of their translation, their orbits being in no way connected with alleged gravitation.

The stellar vortexes that form part of these expanding galaxies are not actuated by a strictly circular motion. On the contrary, the expansion of the vortex manifests itself by the distance that progressively increases between the particles of which it is composed, with the result that these—and the planets carried along with them—do not follow closed orbits, but spirals which gradually draw them away from the sun. This will be dealt with again in Chapter Six, which is devoted to the evolution of the Earth. But first, it will be necessary to examine more closely the consequences of the rotation of the celestial bodies, particularly that of the sun.

3. Expulsion of planets by the sun and of satellites by the planets

As has been seen, the constituent particles of the Universe are of a dynamic nature, their internal movement being expressed by the progressive deformation of the particle which flattens at the poles and expands at the equator. This expansion of all particles is at the root of universal expansion. Obviously a celestial body formed by such particles and actuated by a rotary motion will not always be of the same shape. Made up of particles that are dynamic and therefore pliable, it is also pliant and the rotary motion that actuates it produces on its mass the same effect as on each of the particles : the sphere changes shape as it becomes flattened. This is a phenomenon that can easily be put to the test in a laboratory : a flexible mass becomes flattened under the effect of rotary motion (see Plate 8).

When all the constituent particles of such a process of deformation are subjected to the same conditions, the reciprocal pressures cause expansion to occur in a continuous and regular manner. However, when a very dense material mass rotates in a less dense medium, the resistance of the latter is no longer in proportion to the expansion of the former and the flattening process therefore very quickly results in the formation of a "hump" which, through the effect of rotation, is soon separated from the mass and expelled into surrounding space (see Plate 8).

This general phenomenon is not a peculiarity of the laboratory but occurs sooner or later whenever any sphere is actuated by a motion of rotation in a less dense medium. In the centre of vortexes, stars are in just such a situation. The rotary motion by which they are actuated deforms them and the deformation process inevitably ends up in the expulsion of a planet. Having returned to a more or less spherical form after this expulsion, the star, still actuated by rotary motion, is once again subjected to deformation. The expulsion of planets by the stars is therefore a periodic phenomenon. The fact that there are not, at the moment, adequate means of ascertaining the presence of planets in all the stellar systems is no reason to conclude, as is frequently done, that the solar system is an exception in the Universe. All systems are subject to the same laws—the laws of motion.

Instead of having come from no one knows where and having been "captured" by the sun, the planets were, in fact, ejected by the sun and their distance from it progressively increases under the influence of spiral motion. Proof of this expulsion and progressive increase in distance is supplied by the present positions of the planets. This will now be studied in more detail.

4. Bode's law

The planets do not occupy just any position in the heart of the solar system; on the contrary, their distance from the sun correspond to a factor-2 geometric progression, that is: 1, 2, 4, 8, 16, 32, 64, at least as far as Uranus. It was the German astronomer, Bode, who postulated, in 1778, the law which now bears his name and concerns the distances of the planets. As a matter of fact, the geometric progression which is repeated seven times in a row has two exceptions: the first, right at the beginning, as it does not start from the sun but from Mercury; the second, after Uranus, where the distance is no longer doubled but remains constant [1]. These two exceptions will be studied in detail later and, as will be seen, in no way weaken the validity of the law since they are in complete conformity with the principle of evolution. But the essential point in Bode's law must first be studied, that is, the factor-2 geometric progression observable between Mercury, Venus, the Earth, Mars, the Asteroids, Jupiter, Saturn and Uranus and consequently affecting eight planets (or groups of planets: the Asteroids).

If this factor-2 geometric progression were only repeated two or three times, it could conceivably be attributed to chance, but the fact that it occurs seven times in connection with eight successive planets unquestionably indicates that it is due to some phenomenon that it would be well to examine.

[1] For practical reasons, and in order to obtain the figure 10 for the Earth-Sun distance, each term in the geometric progression is multiplied by 3. The fixed number representing the Mercury-Sun distance is therefore 4, which gives the table below. As the Earth-Sun distance represented by the figure 10 is 148 million kilometres, the figure 1 in Bode's law accordingly corresponds to 14.8 million kilometres.

Distances of planets from the Sun according to Bode's law

Planets	Geometric progression	Triple	Relative distance	Distance in millions of kms According to Bode	Calculated by astronomers
Mercury	$0 \times 3 =$	$0 + 4 =$	$4 \times 14.8 =$	59	58
Venus	1	3	7	104	108
The Earth	2	6	10	148	149
Mars	4	12	16	237	227
The Asteroids	8	24	28	414	410
Jupiter	16	48	52	770	777
Saturn	32	96	100	1480	1426
Uranus	64	192	196	2900	2869
Neptune	128	384	388	5742	4395
Pluto	256	768	772	11426	5898

Since the time it was first put forward nearly two centuries ago, this law has not failed to intrigue astronomers. In fact, it was considered a divine law to such an extent that Le Verrier used it as the basis for all the calculations by which he hoped to establish the position of the planet that perturbed Uranus' course.

The best known of the various astronomers who tried to clarify the problem raised by this geometric progression was Laplace, a contemporary of Bode, who propounded the theory that the sun and the planets had been formed by the condensation of a nebula which, during the process of contraction, left behind it successive rings ; these in their turn contracted and became planets. Various objections were raised to this theory during the Nineteenth Century and a new one was put forward based on an alleged catastrophe provoked by a star passing too close to the sun. It was supposed to have attracted from the sun a jet of matter that became condensed into planets. This theory was also refuted as, in such a case, the planets would have remained at a very short distance from the sun. Accordingly, Laplace's theory was taken up again and developed, with variations, during the Twentieth Century by numerous scientists who contradicted one another, none of the theories put forward being really satisfactory. (This subject has already been studied in fuller detail [1].)

Such a setback is not surprising as all these theories contain the same flaw : they are based on a unique phenomenon, whether creation by condensation or catastrophe. Now, if the factor-2 geometric progression is put in its proper context, that is, the context of evolution, it will be seen to be the result of periodic emission of planets by the sun and of their progressive increase in distance from the sun throughout the ages—past, present and to come. What is actually happening ?

[1] *Eléments de physique évolutive*, Chapter Two, Section 3, Editions du Scorpion, Paris, and *La Terre s'en va*, Appendix II, Editions de la Table Ronde, Paris, both by Louis JACOT.

Every planet expelled by the sun is swept along in the spiral motion of the ambient medium. Now, the heart of the spiral is controlled by a centrifugal force proportional to the radius. As a result, the planet at Distance 1 from the sun moves, over a given period, to Distance 2, the planet at Distance 2 passes to Distance 4, that at Distance 4 to Distance 8, etc. The planets have therefore not been expelled all at the same time and consequently are not all of the same age. The furthest removed are the oldest and the closest are the most recent. Although they were all produced by the sun, they are not, as planetary units, all at the same stage of evolution. The significance of this will be seen later.

The existence, in the heart of the solar vortex, of a centrifugal force proportional to the radius is not idle speculation. Various spectacular phenomena already pointed in this direction. For example, the tails of comets do not follow the nucleus, in spite of the velocity of these celestial bodies, but are thrust away from the sun. Astronomers have called this force "radiation pressure", but this is a mere quibble. A force originating from a central point is a centrifugal force. It has never been given its proper name because it had the serious disadvantage of not being in accord with Newton's theory that all bodies in the solar system are attracted by the sun. In short, a convenient label was used to cover up this brazen infringement of the formal laws of celestial mechanics.

A second proof of the existence of centrifugal force within the solar system is available, less spectacular perhaps but just as clear, and with the additional advantage of enabling the force in question to be calculated—that is, the velocity of translation of the planets. This velocity diminishes with the planet's increase in distance from the sun, as established in certain laws expounded by Kepler [1].

---

[1] One of these laws is generally worded as follows: "The radius vector joining each planet with the sun describes equal areas in equal times." The other is: "The cubes of the mean distances of the planets from the sun are proportional to the squares of their times of revolution."

The force tending towards the exterior diminishes as much as that in the circular direction, centrifugal force consequently being inversely proportional to rotation force. The decrease in velocity of the planets, according to Kepler's laws, therefore indicates that centrifugal force increases in proportion to the distance separating the planets from the sun [1].

As they are continually thrust towards the exterior during their course around the sun by the centrifugal force in the centre of the vortex, the planets do not describe closed orbits, as assumed by Newton's law, but increase their distance from the sun with each revolution. The extent of this increase in distance will be studied in more detail later (Chapter Six, Section 11).

The explanations of Bode's law, given without taking evolution into account, contain yet more flaws. For example, the theory of the condensation of a nebula is in flagrant contradiction to the general trend of evolution which is expansion (and not contraction) of the celestial bodies. As to the explanation based on a catastrophe, this completely ignores the repetitive pattern of the phenomenon, as indicated by the satellites expelled by the planets. It would really be giving too much credence to the theory of catastrophe if it were supposed that all the planets surrounded by satellites had also been visited by celestial bodies that had dragged from them a part of their substance.

As the expulsion of planets by the sun is due to the latter's rotation, a similar phenomenon should occur when a planet begins to rotate on its own axis. This is precisely the case. And perhaps one day astronomers will be able to observe the expulsion of a satellite by a planet. At that point, they will finally understand the senselessness of the so-called theory of gravitation.

As the expulsion of satellites is, for the same reason as that of the planets, a periodic phenomenon, Bode's law should also be observable in their case. And this is exactly so with those of the

[1] For more details, see *La Terre s'en va*, by Louis JACOT, Appendix III, "Kepler's Laws." Editions de La Table Ronde, Paris.

planets, such as Jupiter and Saturn, that have a large number of satellites [1]. However, the law here is a little less precise than between the planets because of the various consequences of evolution on the motion, volume and cohesion of the planets, as will be seen later. First, a more detailed study must be made of the two exceptions to the factor-2 geometric progression noted above.

The first exception concerns the beginning of the progression, which does not start from the sun but from Mercury. Consequently, to obtain the exact distance of the planets, Bode was obliged to add to each term of the factor-2 geometric progression a fixed number representing the sun-Mercury distance. This is altogether logical in view of the fact that the planets were expelled by the sun. This expulsion was clearly a very violent process resulting in the planet being flung out to a great distance. It is quite normal that this unique occurrence in the life of a planet— that is, its creation—would not form part of the regular moving away that can be observed later in the course of its existence. The fixed number that Bode was obliged to add, right from the start, in order that the geometric progression would correspond to the exact distances of the planets is therefore perfectly understandable. It can be regarded, in fact, as unquestionable proof of the expulsion itself. Once evolution in the form of expansion is accepted, it is clear that the planets would not be continuously increasing their distances from the sun unless the sun had been their original starting-point.

Consequently, the idea of expulsion of planets by the sun is not an unfounded theory. In the first place, it is confirmed by the general phenomenon of the progressive deformation of a mass in rotation, resulting in the tearing away and expulsion of a fragment, as already demonstrated by Poincaré. This deformation process governs all masses in rotation. The second proof lies in the fixed number that has to be added to the factor-2 geometric

[1] For fuller details of Bode's law as applied to the satellites, see *La Terre s'en va* by Louis JACOT, Appendix II, (Editions de la Table Ronde, Paris.)

progression in order to obtain the exact position of the planets. Another very important point is Mercury's extraordinary eccentricity. At its perihelion, it is as close as 46 million kilometres to the sun ; it then withdraws and at its aphelion is as much as 70 million kilometres away. This unusual eccentricity, which is not observable to a similar degree in any other planet, is due, as might well be supposed, to the fact that Mercury has only relatively recently been expelled by the sun. This eccentricity will diminish progressively, with time, as the planet follows more and more the same path as the surrounding medium. An even more characteristic phenomenon is the path followed by Phobos, a satellite of Mars, which appears to have been expelled even more recently and revolves around Mars much more rapidly than the planet itself rotates, that is in 7 h. 39 m. whereas a single rotation of Mars takes 24 h. 37 m. Such peculiarities, which Newton's law is quite unable to explain, become clear as soon as an exact idea of the process of evolution in the heart of the solar system, is grasped. Their concordance constitutes undeniable proof of this evolution.

Another peculiarity worth noting is the presence in the solar system of an accumulation of planet debris (the Asteroids) between Mars and Jupiter. Strange concordance : Saturn's ring is also formed of debris—that of a satellite. Should not this presence of debris as much among the satellites as amongst the planets be attributed to causes of a similar nature ? In view of the enormous volume of the mass expelled by a celestial body, is it not probable that certain forces of resistance to the splitting process sometimes result in more or less large fragments becoming detached and being flung out successively instead of in one mass as a single body ?

Now for the second exception to Bode's law. Beyond Uranus, the distance between the planets no longer increases in conformity with a factor-2 geometric progression. According to the law, as Uranus is about 3 milliard kilometres away from the sun, Neptune should be 6 milliard kilometres away and Pluto should be twice Neptune's distance away, that is 12 milliard kilometres. But roughly, Uranus is 3 milliard kilometres away from the sun, Neptune 4.5 milliard and Pluto 6 milliard. In other words, from Uranus onwards, the increase in distance of the planets from the sun during a given time is the same, that is, approximately 1.500 million kilometres or 1.5 milliard. What is the reason for this change of rhythm?

Up to Uranus, all the planets revolve around the sun and rotate on their own axes in the same direction as the sun, i.e. the "direct" or "forward" direction. Uranus, on the contrary, rotates in the opposite direction, called the "retrograde" or "backward" direction. Its position, furthermore, is quite unusual. Whereas all the others rotate "standing", that is to say, around an axis more or less perpendicular to the plane in which they move, Uranus, on the contrary, is in a "lying" position and advances by rolling around on its equator, one of its poles facing the sun at each solstice. What is the reason for this unusual position?

It has already been seen that the spiral motion (in a vortex not disturbed by violent currents) becomes progressively deformed through the effect of centrifugal force and, thrusting towards the exterior, finally exhibits a reversal of its peripheric motion. In other words, the trend in an outward direction develops until it reaches a point at which, in view of the resistance offered by the surrounding medium, it cannot avoid going into reverse. The same applies to the solar vortex which, rotating in a forward direction from the sun up to Uranus, changes direction from that planet onwards. Uranus, which rotated in a forward direction up to that point, is now beginning to somersault, its south pole becoming the north and vice versa. Its rotation is accordingly changing from the direct to the retrograde direction. This reversal in the direction of rotation is a sure sign of change in the direction of the spiral motion and consequently in the direction of the translation of the planets. As the vortex constitutes an overall structure in which all the particles touch and carry each other along, the change from the forward to the backward direction is not as clear-cut as might at first be supposed and, at a distance, it is very difficult to distinguish a backward from a slower forward motion. Nevertheless, the reversal of rotation eliminates all doubts.

The change in the direction of the spiral motion at a certain distance from the centre is not peculiar to the solar vortex. The same can be observed in well-advanced planetary vortexes such as Jupiter in which the nearer satellites are moving in the forward direction whereas the more remote ones exhibit retrograde motion. The astronomer Milne, who has studied a large number of galaxies, also noted, in many of them, a peripheral motion contrary to that at the centre. In short, regardless of the level under consideration —galactic, solar or planetary—a change in the direction of the spiral motion is noted at a certain distance from the centre.

This change of direction appreciably modifies the centrifugal conditions at the heart of the vortex. In the middle, the trend of a particle in an outward direction is backed up by that of the particle closer to the centre, which is moving in the same direction. This makes it clear that centrifugal force increases with distance and is proportional to the radius. But when the spiral motion changes direction, the centrifugal trend of the peripheral particles is no longer reinforced by that of the central particles, since the former are no longer moving in the same direction. Also it must not be forgotten that a vortex is surrounded by many others, each restrained by the expansion of its neighbours. Accordingly, individual expansion becomes uniform, in conformity with overall universal expansion. The exception to the factor-2 geometric progression noted in Neptune and Pluto is therefore entirely in accord with general evolution as expounded by Hubble's law ; geometric progression, in fact, applies, and *can* only apply to the centres of vortexes, because of the particular conditions of centrifugal force obtaining there.

Having been considered a hard and fast law, proof of the divine order of things, Bode's law fell into disrepute the day astronomers noted that the geometric progression did not apply beyond Uranus. From then on, it was no longer considered a law but an approximation devoid of significance. This is an inadmissible conclusion based, as it is, on the preconceived idea that everything in the Universe is repeated indefinitely according to rigid rules. It claims, *a priori*, the permanence of the Universe, and can only lead to errors.

Bode's law is still the general law of evolution of the solar system, just as Hubble's law is the law of the galaxies. Both are fundamental laws substantiating the same phenomenon, but at different scales.

The two exceptions to the factor-2 geometric progression should therefore not be considered as defects invalidating the law but rather as the means of getting closer to the facts and ascertaining the exact conditions of evolution.

In the absence of such knowledge, the motion of the planets and satellites remains completely incomprehensible. There is, in particular, no explanation for the fact that the Earth, Mars, Jupiter and Saturn rotate in the forward direction, whereas the rotation of Uranus, Neptune and probably Pluto is retrograde; nor why the Earth's and Mars' satellites move in the forward direction, those of Uranus and Neptune in the backward, while, in the case of Jupiter and Saturn in between, the motion of the nearest satellites is direct whilst that of the more remote is retrograde. This mystery is only clarified by a study of spiral motions.

5. Expansion and decay of planets

At first, the appearance of the various planets is disconcerting. While Mercury, Venus and Mars are less voluminous than the Earth, and the Asteroids between Mars and Jupiter are formed by the debris of a disintegrated planet, Jupiter is so voluminous and of such low density that its speed of rotation is not the same at the poles as at the equator. Saturn is also very voluminous and appears to lack cohesion. Beyond that point, the volume of the planets begins to decrease rapidly, Pluto being nothing more than a tiny body. In other words, each planet has its own special character.

All these differences and many more are easily accounted for by the conditions existing in the heart of a vortex.

When a planet is expelled by the sun, it is swept up in the solar vortex, the particles of which are subject to much greater pressure at the centre than at the periphery (cf. Chapter Four, Section 2). It is accordingly highly compressed by the ambient medium which carries it along and holds it as in a vise. At this stage, it is small and dense and revolves around the sun, to which it always presents the same face. It consequently does not rotate on its own axis. This is, at the moment, the case with Mercury and probably also with Venus. As they do not rotate, they do not expel satellites and therefore have none.

As it is thrust progressively away from the sun through centrifugal force, the planet moves into a less dense medium. The concentric pressure to which it is subjected accordingly diminishes and its volume increases. The greater the diameter of the planet, the greater the difference in the velocity of the ambient medium on its diurnal and nocturnal faces. The medium on the latter side, being further removed from the sun, moves around the planet more slowly (Kepler's laws). This lag in the velocity of the ambient medium on the nocturnal as opposed to the diurnal face inevitably causes it to rotate. To understand what occurs in such cases, one needs only hold a pencil between the hands and move them either in opposite directions or in the same direction but at different speeds. Inevitably, the pencil will be subjected to a rotating movement. In short, carried along at different speeds on its two faces, the planet begins to turn on its own axis and a planetary vortex is consequently formed in the heart of the solar vortex. The central part of this new spiral will turn in a forward direction, that is, in the same direction as the solar vortex, whereas the peripheral area will have a retrograde motion corresponding to the difference in speed of the two media in which it is being carried along. This explains why the Earth, Mars, Jupiter and Saturn rotate in a forward direction, why they have satellites and why these satellites move in a forward direction when they are close to their planet and in a backward direction when they are far removed.

The decrease in pressure to which the planets are subjected as they move progressively away from the sun produces considerable increase in their volume. Jupiter is accordingly 1,300 times more voluminous than the Earth. This increase in volume results in an appreciable decrease in the density of the planet which appears to have become essentially gaseous and to be no longer sufficiently cohesive to turn as a block on its own axis, its period of rotation ranging from 9 h. 50 m. at the equator to approximately 9 h. 55 m. in the polar regions. In fact, there is even a difference between the south and the north.

In spite of its enormous size, Jupiter therefore takes half as much time as the Earth (24 hours) to turn on its own axis. This phenomenon, puzzling at first, can be explained precisely by the unusual proportions of the planet. According to Kepler's laws, the greater the diameter of the planetary vortex, the more noticeable the velocity differences at the various points of the solar vortex, and consequently the more rapid the rotation. (The quicker one hand is moved in relation to the other, the faster the pencil rotates.)

In view of the fact that pressure in the spiral area diminishes towards the periphery, the volume of the planets should, strictly speaking, increase as they move away from the centre. Now, from Saturn onwards, on the contrary, it diminishes from one planet to the other. This seems at first to contradict the theory of evolution but it can easily be explained by sticking more closely to the facts. Obviously a planet that periodically expels satellites loses, each time, a part of its mass. It therefore cannot grow indefinitely. In addition, it must not be forgotten that matter and ether particles are of the same nature, matter being condensed ether. This condensation is due to the fact that the particles in the centre of the vortexes are more compressed than those at the periphery. With increase in distance from the centre, the material particles are subjected more and more to the same conditions as the ether particles. As a result, evolution of the planets is accompanied by progressive disintegration of the atoms which little by little resemble the indistinguishable medium in which they are carried along. In short, planets and satellites lose their individuality and finally melt into the overall substance of the vortex which absorbs them.

In accordance with the evolutionary process, the period of expansion of a planet is accordingly inevitably followed by a period of decay. This is particularly noticeable from Uranus onwards, where the somersaulting of the planet, due to change of motion, subjects it and its satellites to a very severe ordeal. From Uranus onwards, the rhythm is completely reversed. The planet and its closest satellites move in a backward direction, those still further removed probably having disappeared at the time of the somersaulting. In the case of the planets beyond Uranus, that is Neptune and Pluto, the cohesion of the planetary vortexes appears to have become so weak that even the closest satellites seem to have been absorbed one after the other by the solar vortex.

In short, only the theory of evolution is capable of appropriately accounting for the position of the planets in the heart of the solar system, for the differences in their volume, translation and rotation, and for the expulsion, position, number and movement of their satellites. This theory also explains the most extraordinary cases, such as Uranus' unusual position, Mercury's extreme eccentricity, Phobos' fantastic speed (it revolves around Mars three times faster than the planet itself rotates), the presence in the solar system of the debris of a planet (the Asteroids) and that of a satellite (Saturn's ring), the thrust of comet tails away from the sun, etc. And at this point, a more detailed study of comets is justified, as they are extremely instructive.

6. Comets

Comets differ from planets by their most unusual appearance (in particular their tails, which are sometimes several million kilometres in length) and by their very eccentric paths.

Comet tails and the nebula envelope surrounding the nucleus indicate that the celestial body is in a state of rapid disintegration. A large number of photographs of comets are available, taken at intervals of a few days. They show the tails splitting up, fragments falling apart and dispersing through space. The distintegration of the body cannot possibly be doubted.

The other characteristic of comets is the eccentricity of their orbits, which are definitely more exaggerated than that of the planets.

Although the majority of these celestial bodies are situated between Mars and Jupiter in the area of the Asteroids, others come from the boundaries of the solar system. Halley's comet, for example, is beyond Neptune at its aphelion and closer to the sun than Mercury at its perihelion. When it passes from one to the other, it necessarily crosses the orbits of Neptune, Uranus, Saturn, Jupiter, the Asteroids, Mars, the Earth, Venus and Mercury. This extremely rapid approach should considerably increase the effect of gravitation, if it existed, and the comet should then inevitably fall into the sun. The fact that, having reached its perihelion, it abruptly resumes its voyage toward the boundaries of the solar system puts the theory of gravitation in its place!

What is the explanation for this difference in the behaviour of the comets as opposed to the planets? There is probably a connection between their two characteristics, and in fact the study that has just been made of conditions in the heart of the solar vortex can account for what happens. As has been seen, the volume of the celestial bodies depends on the pressure exerted on them by the ambient medium. The planets, having almost completely circular orbits, are subjected to only a very slow decrease in pressure as, from one orbit to the other, their movement away from the sun is relatively small.   The increase in their volume and decrease in their density and cohesion—in other words, the various stages in the general process of disintegration—consequently occur very slowly.   As the planets remain more or less in the same medium, the latter compresses the light gaseous elements against their solid globes and thereby prevents them from forming either nebulous envelopes or tails.   Conditions are quite different in the case of the comets.   As a result of their eccentric orbits, they travel rapidly through media of widely varying densities in which they are subjected to sometimes very strong, sometimes very weak pressures resulting in disintegration as rapid as it is generalized.   As comets, unlike planets, are not continually surrounded by the same medium compressing the light gaseous elements against the solid nucleus, these are blown in a direction opposed to the sun by what astronomers call "radiation pressure".   The sight of comet tails, thrust away from the sun, is striking evidence of the existence of centrifugal force, as opposed to gravitation, in the heart of the solar system.

But why do comets have such eccentric orbits ?   Take the case of those in the Asteroids' area, which are unquestionably the debris of a planet.   It is possible that at the time of the planet's expulsion by the sun, the separation did not occur in one solid mass but in various bits of debris flung out in the form of an enormous spray, the individual parts of which began to describe individual orbits according to the conditions of their expulsion. At the time of its creation, a planet at first describes an orbit that is appreciably more eccentric than later on, as can be seen in the example of Mercury.   This is an unavoidable effect of the expulsion process.   In other words, the planetoids and comets between the orbits of Mars and Jupiter are all of the same origin—they come from a planet that broke up at the moment it was expelled from the sun.   If certain fragments constitute small planets (without tails) and others comets (with tails), the difference is due to the trajectories they were obliged to adopt at the time of their expulsion.

The origin of the comets coming from the peripheral area of the solar system is also easily explained by the evolution of the planets and satellites described above.   As was seen, the planets' satellites were swept up one after the other by the solar vortex. Now, a satellite describes around its planet an orbit whose radius is very short when compared to that of the solar vortex.   When it leaves its planetary orbit, the satellite necessarily describes a trajectory which is the resultant of its former planetary motion and that of the solar vortex—that is, a very elongated orbit stretching from the centre of the vortex to its periphery.   Comets coming from the peripheral areas are therefore the remains of former planetary systems.   Their spectacular disintegration gives a striking idea of the fate that awaits the planets.

CHAPTER VI

EVOLUTION OF THE EARTH

1. Proofs of Earth's evolution

The theory of the evolution of our planet—already put forward in antiquity—became a certainty for geologists and paleontologists as soon as they undertook a methodical study of strata and fossils. These scientists noticed, in the course of their work, that the ground covering the globe consisted of distinct, superimposed layers extending several hundred metres in depth, each with its particular character and fossils. By systematic investigation, geologists managed to classify these according to age. They divided the Earth's past history into four eras: Primary, Secondary, Tertiary and Quaternary; these in turn were divided into periods (of time) or systems (of rock), generally four or five per era, corresponding to the various strata. Finally, for professional purposes, these systems were subdivided into stages (about sixty).

This classification of the ground according to age is extremely important as it is clear from the fossils in the different layers that the Earth's flora and fauna were not always the same, but were unquestionably subject to evolution. Certain species appeared a long time after others—Man being the most recent—whereas several, though at one time widespread (for example, the big reptiles of the Secondary era), disappeared completely. In short, since these discoveries, the Earth's evolution is no longer a matter of conjecture but of fact.

These changes in flora and fauna did not occur without cause; they were the result of changes in conditions—conditions that are incidentally confirmed in the terrain. What explanation can be offered for the existence, throughout the ages, of such a series of geological strata very different one from the other?

Carrying their investigations further, geologists discovered that beneath these strata the ground, whether crystalline or cristallophyllian, no longer formed distinct layers. Why this difference?

Other discoveries were no less astonishing. For example, the climate was quite different in the past from what it is today. At certain periods, scorching heat completely dried up extensive sea areas, tropical vegetation stretching as far as Spitzbergen, as indicated by coal deposits; at others, glacial caps more than a thousand metres thick covered immense areas of what are now temperate zones. In addition, immersions and emersions modified the shorelines. Continents shifted, as was authoritatively demonstrated by Wegener. Chains of mountains were formed, then disappeared from the surface of the Earth through erosion. What was the cause of all these changes?

Different theories were put forward to explain these phenomena—modifications in solar activity, displacement of the poles, contraction of the globe following its cooling down, etc.—but apart from the fact that they only shifted the problem (Why would solar activity be subjected to such variations? Why would the poles change position? Why would the Earth contract?) and confined themselves to considering a particular case, none was acceptable because none was in harmony with the broad lines of universal evolution. And clearly, the Earth's evolution cannot have been different from that of the Universe in general and of the solar system in particular.

Just as evolution of the solar system has to be studied in the context of that of the galaxies, so evolution of our planet has to be in accord with that of the solar system.

Accordingly, it will now be necessary to ascertain if geological findings tally with the general astronomic laws of evolution. For this purpose, the various stages through which our planet has passed in the course of its existence must be reviewed.

2. *Translation without rotation*

As the Earth is a product of the sun and moves progressively away from it, the best means of understanding the conditions that existed in the past is to study the younger planets which, as is the case with Mercury and Venus, are now in positions formerly occupied by the Earth.

As has been seen, our planet, at the time of its creation, was compressed by the very dense ambient medium and moved along its solar orbit in such fashion that the same side always faced the sun. (This is particularly the case, at the moment, with Mercury.) Consequently conditions on the surface of the globe scarcely changed through the ages. Increasing distance from the sun slightly modified the intensity of solar radiation, but this was a very slow process. Climatic conditions therefore remained practically the same for each of the hemispheres, the one facing the sun being subjected to scorching heat, the one lost in endless night being cold in spite of the sun's proximity. Only in those twilight areas where day and night merged into one another—the poles, for example—can there have been periodic climatic changes due to the inclination of the Earth's axis which caused them to move alternately from light into darkness during one translation around the sun. But apart from these regions, conditions remained practically unchanged in both hemispheres. It was therefore not possible for different geological layers to form during this entire period, which lasted a very long time. It extended beyond Mercury's present stage and probably even up to the position at present occupied by Venus.

It will now be clear why the ground of this—the Archean—
age, which is anterior to the Primary era, does not contain various
strata. The reason for the main structural difference between
Archean ground and the sedimentary rocks of later periods will
also be clear.

3. Earth's slow rotation

Passing into a less dense medium, the Earth, no longer so
tightly compressed, began to free itself. The difference in the
velocity of the ambient medium, faster on its lighted side (because
closer to the sun) than on its hidden face (Kepler's laws), imposed
on the planet a rotational movement which, in the early stages,
must have been quite slow. It is logical to assume that as the
Earth, like Mercury at the moment, had no rotation of its own,
it did not suddenly start turning on its own axis in about 24 hours
as it does today. It was only gradually that the decrease in
pressure of the ambient medium was felt and also only gradually
that the planet started to turn on its own axis.

This slow rotation, which took the place of translation without
rotation, entirely altered conditions on the surface of the globe.
The area which had hitherto been in darkness little by little moved
into the light while the lighted area moved into obscurity. A
radical change accordingly took place in the climate of each
specific area and was responsible for the formation of the different
geological strata. As one single rotation probably lasted thousands of years, this stratification process was sometimes considerable
and accounts for the superimposition of the layers that followed
the Archean age and constituted the beginning of the Primary era.

Conditions existing at that time on the Earth must be clearly
understood. Nowadays, a 24-hour rotation produces a very rapid
succession in day and night (365 rotations in one year), the differences in climate being due to the inclination of the Earth's axis.
But at the time of slow rotation, the seasons were exclusively the

result of the change from light to darkness and were therefore due to rotation and not to translation. The result was a very hard winter of darkness lasting thousands of years, a summer of unbearable heat in the antipodes for a similarly long period, and in between, in the dawn and twilight areas, two intermediate zones. This succession of seasons, differing widely one from the other, is responsible for the distinctive character of the various geological strata.

Common characteristics are noted as between rotations because obviously two strata formed during two summer periods, when entire seas were evaporated and left behind immense deposits of salt and gypsum, look much more alike than two consecutive strata showing the effects of summer and autumn or autumn and winter.

These common characteristics resulting from the cyclic evolution of the seasons due to rotation have made it possible to draw up a table of the history of the Earth (Section 13 below) in which the different periods are not only listed in their chronological order but also classified according to the rotation point to which they correspond, i. e. summer (or midday position), winter (or midnight position), spring (or dawn position) and autumn (or twilight position). There are several advantages in this arrangement. First of all, it makes it possible to establish how many slow rotations of the Earth on its own axis took place during former ages. It also eliminates a certain number of misunderstandings regarding terrain classification. Geologists have, in fact, agreed that the Cambrian, Silurian, Devonian, Carboniferous, Triassic, Jurassic, Cretaceous, etc., periods succeeded each other in that order. This is true for the same region all the time, but if a comparison is made of areas in different longitudes, it is no longer the case. For example, in one hemisphere, the Jurassic period corresponds to the midday position, but at the same moment the area following it in rotation is actually in the dawn position, therefore in the Triassic period, while the area preceding it has already moved into the twilight position and is therefore in the Cretaceous period. In these different regions, the Triassic, Jurassic and Cretaceous periods accordingly occurred simultaneously.

Serious error in interpreting the facts can be avoided if this is understood. Various geologists, for example, on the basis of studies of terrain, have stated that certain mountain chains parallel to the equator were formed first in the west and then in the east in the course of later geological periods. They inferred that the upheaval of mountain chains had been a very slow process lasting several thousand years. Such a conclusion is in outright contradiction to tectonic principles. These enormous masses that rise up and then sink back again forming folds cannot have taken thousands of years to subside. The movement was rapid and abrupt, like that of earthquakes. If it appears to be older in the west than in the east, that is merely because the incident that occurred simultaneously across vast areas in different longitudes left its mark in strata that were not all in the same stage of evolution, those in the west moving into the light after those in the east. In other words, the western region was still only in the Triassic period when the central region was in the Jurassic period and the eastern in the Cretaceous. The fold formed in the Triassic consequently seems to be of earlier origin in the west, but this is fallacious. An earthquake recorded at midday today in Europe would be recorded five hours earlier in New York, because New York time is behind that of Europe. But this in no way implies that the earthquake affected America five hours earlier than Europe.

Plate 10 shows a photograph of Syltoppene terrain in Greenland where not only is the superimposition of layers particularly noticeable but also their cyclic repetition. Alternate light and dark strata, proof of alternation in the seasons through the ages, are clearly visible. Within the light layers, there are distinct variations in intensity corresponding to variations in light during one translation around the sun as a consequence of the inclination of the Earth's axis. Such strata are invaluable calendars for calculating the ages of the different layers.

4. Evolution of climates

Today, climatic areas vary one from the other according to latitude—hot at the equator, cold at the poles and temperate in the intermediate zones. Paleontologists affirm, however, that it was quite different in former ages when, at certain periods, Arctic fauna existed as far south as the Mediterranean and, at others, tropical vegetation was found as far north as Spitzbergen. This is an extraordinary fact that requires clarification.

Another strange thing is that the climates of different areas varied through the ages to an unusual degree. What are today temperate zones were subjected, at certain periods, to such extreme heat (for centuries at a time) that very large inland seas completely evaporated. What is more surprising is that these long periods of torrid heat were followed by equally long periods of intense cold. These climatic variations were repeated so often that their cyclic nature can no longer be doubted.

The last mystery to be solved in this connection is the fact that certain species, fauna as well as flora, frequently lived in all latitudes from the equator to the Arctic and Antarctic circles.

These various peculiarities have been attributed to wide variations in solar radiation. But to what are the cyclic changes due? And if solar radiation is the answer, how is it possible that the same species were found from the poles to the equator? Displacement of the poles has also been put forward, but this theory does not take into account the fact that the same species lived simultaneously at the poles *and* at the equator.

Instead of falling back on purely imaginary cosmic or geological events to explain these mysteries, full significance should be given to the two principle factors responsible for variations of temperature on the surface of the Earth : they were, are, and always will be, the planet's translation around the sun and its rotation. The former produces the seasons—spring, summer, autumn, winter— as a consequence of the inclination of the Earth's axis ; the latter is responsible for the succession in light and darkness, for nocturnal cooling down and diurnal reheating.

The fact that the Earth at present turns on its own axis in 24 hours is not sufficient reason to suppose that this has always been the case. Permanence is not of this world and 24-hour rotation is in no way a general law of the solar system. All the planets have their own particular and distinctive motions as a result of their individual positions within the solar vortex which carries them along.

As has already been seen, a planet expelled by the sun begins to turn around it, showing always the same face (as Mercury is doing at present). This is due to the very high pressure to which it is subjected by the solar vortex. The hemisphere facing the sun is exposed, without interruption, to the heat of the solar rays whereas the hemisphere in darkness, in spite of the sun's proximity, is bitterly cold because the solar rays never reach it. Between these two extremes situated, at the midday and midnight positions in rotation, there is an intermediate area corresponding to a line drawn around the Earth through the poles and crossing the equator twice, once at the dawn position and once at the twilight. This area has been called the "crown of life" as it was favourable to the development of life. It had the advantage of light without too intense heat and of a temperature halfway between that of the midday and midnight positions.

Once the planet started turning slowly on its own axis, this favourable area began to shift across the surface of the globe.

Now, as the Earth turns 365 times on its own axis in the course of one translation around the sun, a day is very much shorter than a year at the present time. Formerly it was the contrary. A day, consisting of one period of light and one of darkness, lasted thousands of years.

These rotation conditions, altogether different from those applying nowadays, explain the climatic peculiarities of former ages. Because of this slow rotation, areas that today are temperate faced the sun for long periods and therefore had extremely hot climates. Then, when that particular hemisphere moved into darkness, polar fauna extended as far as the equator.

Slow rotation also explains the periodicity of climates which were alternately very hot and very cold. These changes of climate in former ages were not haphazard but constituted a cyclic phenomenon that could only be produced by a cyclic cause.

Finally, slow rotation explains particularly clearly the presence of the same species from the poles to the equator during one and the same geological period. The climatic conditions on the basis of which periods are established corresponded to longitude. The "crown of life", as much at the dawn as at the twilight positions of the globe, more or less followed longitude and profited in its entirety from approximately the same intensity of solar radiation. The same species were accordingly able to live just as well at the poles as at the equator.

It is very interesting to follow the development of flora and fauna in relation to the slow rotation of the Earth. Any number of enigmas are cleared up in this way. For example, certain echinoderms of the Primary era disappeared completely in the Triassic and Jurassic periods and reappeared suddenly in the Cretaceous. This would be inexplicable if each geological stratum represented the same period for the entire Earth, as two successive creations are not logical. But if the Earth's slow rotation is followed, it is clear that certain species remained in the same position on the globe in relation to solar light. In other words, they did not follow their original habitat in its rotation; it caught up with them again after one complete turn. This is why their remains are found in terrains of the same area but in later strata, with a break in the intermediate layers. Another example : certain species, characteristic of a certain period in a certain area, were found elsewhere in terrains of a later period, but not in the strata of the intervening period. Here again, the explanation is to be found by following the "crown of life" on the face of the globe : starting at the equator in the dawn position, it stretched, with the characteristic features of a given period, as far as the poles ; it then continued on the other side of the hemisphere back to the equator at the twilight position with the characteristic features of a later period. The same species were accordingly found in the terrains of two different periods (at the dawn and twilight positions) but not in the intermediate strata of the periods corresponding to the midday and midnight positions and therefore subject to too high or too low temperature.

It has now been clearly demonstrated that climate evolved on the Earth through the ages. These changes could only occur in the context of the evolution of the planet, the velocity of rotation of which became modified with time. And it was precisely the slowness of the rotation in the early eras that caused the cyclic modifications of temperature.

5. *Glacial and inter-glacial periods*

One of the most characteristic phenomena of this cyclic evolution in climate was the formation of glacial caps over enormous areas of what are now temperate regions. There is no doubt about the existence of these glacial formations. It is well known that moraines with characteristic features are formed on the edges of glaciers. This has enabled the limits of former glaciers to be determined with accuracy. The same applies to the thickness of the ice. Erratic blocks are found in the Jura Mountains up to an altitude of approximately 1,050 metres. These granite blocks are of quite different composition from the limestone on which they lie. There is no doubt that they were carried there by the glaciers which completely covered the Swiss plateau. The difference in altitude between the bed of Lake Neuchâtel, which is at less than 300 metres, and the highest level of the moraine (1,050 metres) represents a thickness of ice of more than 750 metres. In other parts of Europe, this thickness exceeded 1,000 metres, and in the United States, 2,000.

These formations extended over considerable areas. In the Quaternary era, for example, the ice covered the whole of Scandinavia, almost the whole of England, Denmark, Holland, North Germany, Poland, the Baltic States and the greater part of Russia. At the same time, the Alpine glaciers completely covered Switzerland and reached as far as Bâle in the north and Lyon in the south. In America, the ice covered the whole of Canada and the northern parts of the United States.

Such glacial formations can only be explained by climatic conditions that are radically different from those of the present time. They constitute irrefutable proof of the evolution of the world and of the fundamental changes that occurred in the factors that caused the climates, that is, in the Earth's translation and rotation. The latter was the cause, in particular, of the cooling down of the hemisphere which had been plunged in darkness for thousands of years.

Only an outmoded geocentrism could attribute this cooling off to variations in solar activity and assume that the Earth is a permanent world capable of recording changes which, in the case of the other celestial bodies, could only take place over periods of thousands of years. The Earth has existed for a much shorter time than the sun and has necessarily been subjected to much more rapid change.

It is not only glacial phenomenon as such that needs to be explained but also its periodicity. There were four glaciation periods during the Quaternary era—that is, since Man's appearance on Earth—which is a relatively short lapse of time. Such rapid evolution excludes not only the theory of a shift in the poles but also that of variations in solar radiation. Periodic changes as rapid as these could not pass unnoticed at the present time.

Glacial phenomena, undeniable and significant, are of the utmost importance for an understanding of world evolution. Any theory that does not take them into account cannot be accepted. They must therefore be studied very closely and partial explanations that do not fall into the overall lines of universal evolution should not be considered satisfactory. All explanations of particular phenomena—this cannot be too strongly emphasized—must fit into the general context of the evolutionary process.

The particular interest of these glacial formations derives from the fact that, occurring in the hemisphere plunged in darkness, they only need to be counted in order to establish the number of times the Earth turned on its own axis in former ages.

Traces of glaciation can be found even below the Algonkian group of rocks in Canada where the Huronian starts in the form of glacial conglomerates in striated blocks. This is not a purely local feature as these traces extend over more than 1,000 kilometres in the region of the Great Lakes.

Glacial formations were also noted at the end of the Algonkian, at various points of the globe. In Norway, in the Jotnian stage beneath the Cambrian marine-overflow system, the sparagmites have all the characteristics of glacial deposits. The same is the case with the Keweenaw deposits in Canada which are very similar to the Jotnian. The tills in China, striated block conglomerates, found in argilagenous soil, certainly represent former moraines of the period. The glaciation extends into Siberia and Kuznetsk. South Africa has not been spared either. Conglomerates with traces of glacial origin form the basis of the Cambrian marine-overflow system, and in Australia, 500-metre-thick fluvioglacial deposits extend over more than 300 kilometres to Lat. 30° S. The presence of glacial formations at points as different as these excludes the theory of polar displacement as, obviously, this could not have carried regions as far apart as Norway, Canada, China, South Africa and Australia at one and the same time into the polar positions.   On the other hand, slow rotation of the Earth would lead all these regions to pass successively into the darkened area of the globe.

As a glaciation is found in both the Lower and Upper Algonkian system of rocks, it can be accepted that during this period the Earth effected one rotation on its own axis.   The change of climate between these two systems is evident.   For example, in the Finnish Algonkian, in the region of Lake Onega, definite coal strata indicate the existence of what was already a very rich vegetation.

However, if the number of glaciations is used to calculate the number of rotations, the results will be found to differ according to the longitude of the different places considered.   Actually, only the regions situated on the darkened face of the globe during the Archean age completed one whole rotation before the following night.   When rotation, which is effected from west to east, began, Asia, which was then in the twilight position, immediately passed into darkness and was subjected to pre-Cambrian glaciation. Europe, more to the west, left the midday position and moved into twilight while America, which was even more to the west, emerged from the borders of darkness and moved into the light. The geological conditions of the pre-Cambrian period therefore differed from one region of the globe to another and only the western area, that is America, experienced a complete Algonkian period covering all the seasons, from the morning position through the midday and twilight points to the night, where it linked up with the Cambrian period.

The Cambrian terrains have a distinctive fauna comprising more than 1,500 species of invertebrata, all marine.   Lower levels, corresponding to the end-of-night position, contain very few fossils. Certain species were blind, others had bulging eyes.   It can therefore be assumed that these had developed in the darkened zone or in very poorly lighted regions. Thereafter, fauna developed considerably. Archaeocytes, the organisms that form reefs and were found from the Antarctic up to the north of Siberia, constitute evidence of the reheating process. The Silurian period, which followed the Cambrian, is conspicuous for its glacial conglomerates, particularly in Norway. Surprisingly, this glacial period left far fewer traces than the preceding ones, but this can be explained by the exceptional marine overflow that occurred in the Cambrian period and covered the greater part of the land areas of the so-called temperate zone. Now, contrary to ice formations on land, the ice formed on the seas does not leave moraines but disappears without lasting traces. Scandinavia appears to have been the only part of Europe above sea level at that period and consequently it is there that glacial conglomerates are found.

The second rotation accordingly included the Cambrian and Silurian periods. In fact, even the Lower Devonian could be added. The change from one system of rocks to another is not very clearly defined. In England, for example, in the transition between the two systems, alternating Devonian and Silurian terrains occur and are frequently separated by bone layers called bone beds. These are thin layers in which the remains of fish and crustacea, killed in mass, indicate sudden invasions of the lagoons by the sea. These alternations can be explained by the fact that the areas near the border between light and darkness, due to the inclination of the Earth's axis, passed alternately from one to the other in the course of one translation around the sun. This is the case even now in the polar regions which, on account of this inclination, have two long seasons in the course of one year—that of summer, or continuous light, and of winter, or uninterrupted night. The passage from darkness to light produced thawing of the ice and annual immersions that entirely modified the flora and fauna. The areas situated at the border between light and darkness will be studied in more detail in connection with coal formation (Chapter Four, Section 11, Subsection 4).

In the mid-Devonian system, deposits in Bohemia, silicified peat bogs in Scotland and petrified forests in the State of New York heralded the rains of the morning position following the thaw, while in the Upper Devonian, desert formations indicated the midday position. The "old red sandstone of the Devonian system" was a continental deposit with very monotonous fauna. On the other hand, the Arctic regions, where solar radiation was less extreme, were covered with lush vegetation. This was the case in Ellesmere Island, the Bear Islands, etc.

In the Carboniferous period, the hot humid climate was very favourable to vegetation. A marine overflow flooded the whole of England where the (marine) Dinantian stage of rocks followed the "old red sandstone" system. As in the Devonian system, the alternation in the layers clearly indicated that the evening position had been reached. This succession of periods of luxuriant growth followed by periods of devastation, characteristic of coal deposits, is particularly noteworthy. For example, in the Sarre-Lorraine coal basin, which is 6,000 metres deep, there are 88 superimposed seams of a total coal thickness of 92 metres. Each of these seams is separated from the next by two different layers, one forming what is known as the roof, the other the wall. (This will be dealt with again later.) The periodicity of these formations indicates how long this region remained at the boundary between light and darkness.

A vast glaciation occurred leaving traces in North America (Squantum tills near Boston), India (Talcher tills), Africa (Dwyka tills), South America (Orleans or Itarare conglomerates), and Australia, where it was found that the glaciers flowed northwards. Although all geologists agree that this glaciation occurred in the Carboniferous period, opinion differs regarding the particular epoch of the period. Certain writers place it in the mid-Carboniferous, others in the Upper. The essential point is its existence, which marked the completion of the third rotation. This accordingly included the Devonian and the Lower and mid-Carboniferous periods.

In the Upper Carboniferous, light was again reached. Vegetation once more developed rapidly but the alternation in light and darkness noted at the twilight position (mid-Carboniferous) started again at the dawn point, i. e. in the Stephanian epoch of the Upper Carboniferous period. As a result, the coal series in the French St.-Etienne basin, 3,500 metres thick, consist of around twenty superimposed seams.

The Permian period which followed was characterized by hot seas containing Fusulina. In Greenland, swagerine, Productus and ammonite faunas were found, the timorite type being widespread as far as Texas and the Sunda Islands. It can be assumed that once more the midday position had been reached. On the North Atlantic continent, sandstone and predominantly red clay formed a combination that has been termed "new red sandstone". The similarity between the "old red sandstone" of the Devonian period and the "new red sandstone" of the Permian implies similarity between the conditions in which they were formed, that is a periodicity in the phenomena. A comparison between the third and fourth slow rotations reveals that the old as much as the new sandstone tallied with the midday position. This is the only acceptable explanation for the desert formations that were caused by torrid climates and occurred between periods of glaciation.

At the end of the Permian period, the Zechstein Sea—a long arm of water extending from Russia, in the east, to England, in the west, across the lowlands of Germany—dried up leaving enormous deposits of salt, gypsum and potash. It was the same in America where the "Great Salt Basin", as it dried up, left similar deposits more than a thousand metres thick.

The climatic disturbances that occurred at the end of this period were responsible for the extermination of a great part of the fauna and flora of the Primary era. It was chiefly this extermination that led geologists to establish a demarcation between the Primary, which terminated with the Permian period, and the Secondary, which began with the Triassic. Traces of glaciation have been discovered in the rock systems corresponding to the end of the Permian and the beginning of the Triassic periods in the Congo and in Australia where, according to Campana and Wilson[1], the Permian glaciation was on a scale comparable to that of the Quaternary era in the Alps. Although traces of glaciation have not, as far as is known, been discovered elsewhere, it is considered that the break between the species of the Primary and Secondary eras is so clearcut that the Triassic period certainly marks the passage into night.

Climatic changes are particularly noticeable in the Russian Permian system where progressive degeneration of the fauna can be observed, as both Gignoux [2] and Moret [3] have pointed out.

The fourth rotation accordingly lasted from the Upper Carboniferous to the Lower Triassic periods and included the entire Permian.

With the fifth rotation started the Secondary era, which included the Triassic, Jurassic and Cretaceous periods. The flora and fauna indicated that the climate was increasingly favourable to life. The Muschelkalk series of limestone rocks of the mid-Triassic period in Germany are particularly rich in shells. Amphibia, such as the Mastodausaurus and the Capitosaurus, lived equally well in Spitzbergen, India and South Africa.

In the Jurassic period, there were coral reefs in abundance as much as 4,000 kilometres north of their present limit. The flora of the Arctic region—Spitzbergen, Franz-Josef Land, Alaska—was that of a very mild climate. In short, this corresponded to the height of the midday position.

The Cretaceous period saw an extraordinary development in reptilia, crocodilia, dinosauria, the varieties of which increased in pace with their size. The monstrous reptiles and sauria of the Secondary era are now familiar to all through reconstructions that have been made.

[1] *Eclogae Geologicae Helvetiae*, 1955, Vol. 48.
[2] *Géologie stratigraphique*, p. 256.
[3] *Paléontologie*, pp. 71 and 72.

It was also in the Cretaceous period that flowering plants appeared for the first time on the Earth. They immediately spread over all the continents. It is probable that their appearance was related to a modification in atmospheric conditions, perhaps a clearing of the air.

A change in climate occurred at the end of the Cretaceous period and caused the disappearance of the greater part of the reptilia. In Greenland, three very distinct, progressively more cold-resistant species of flora succeeded each other [1]. The same phenomenon took place in the seas. The orbitolines, peculiar to hot seas, which first appeared in France at the peak of the Jurassic period and then flourished from the beginning of the Cretaceous, disappeared in the Turonian epoch of the mid-Upper Cretaceous period.

Although the Earth made several rotations during the Primary era, it effected only one during the Secondary. This era accordingly corresponded to the fifth rotation which included the Triassic, Jurassic and Cretaceous periods. The Lower Eocene tallied with the beginning of the night. Extensive glaciations are not noted at this period—it must not be forgotten that terrain is always subject to erosion after its formation—but unquestionable proof of the cooling-off process is nevertheless to be found in the progressive changes that occurred in fauna and flora. Thereafter the total disappearance of the majority of the large reptiles and the appearance of a new fauna in the Tertiary era are sure signs of a very definite break.

Geologists have divided the Tertiary into Eocene, Oligocene, Miocene and Pliocene periods. A rapid reheating occurred, beginning in the Lower Eocene period. In the mid-Eocene (Lutetian epoch), palm trees grew in France and England. The flora (magnolia, etc.) of relatively hot countries extended up to Spitzbergen and Greenland. In the Upper Eocene period, the sea

---

[1] FURON, *Paléogéographie*, p. 277.

withdrew from the Paris basin, leaving behind the large gypsum deposits of the Ludian stage. The thick phosphate deposits of North Africa were also formed during this epoch. It was accordingly a time of intense evaporation. In South America, the heat-resisting flora extended progressively in the direction of Antarctica. During the Eocene and Oligocene periods, the araucaria grew in Patagonia, Kerguelen Island, Antarctica and New Zealand. The reheating process extended from pole to pole. This was the mid-summer point and the Oligocene period therefore marked the midday position.

The climate of the Miocene period was definitely less hot than that of the Oligocene. Northern flora spread over France, the limit of palm trees withdrew more and more towards the south and equatorial species were replaced by deciduous-type trees, such as beech, birch, etc.

In the Tertiary era, mammals developed considerably, as the reptiles had done in the Secondary. This evolution in the species undoubtedly corresponds to an evolution in the climatic conditions and a decrease in the intensity of solar radiation on the surface of the Earth.

At the end of the Pliocene period, from one end of Asia to the other, from eastern China to Turkestan, deserts were formed in the closed basins. The large lakes of Mongolia dried up, subsequent to which extensive glaciation drove the fauna southwards.

In Europe, the glaciation which marked the end of the sixth revolution and the passage from the Tertiary to the Quaternary era is generally called the Günz glaciation.

In the Quaternary, Man made his first appearance. Now, as has already been noted [1], one rotation of the Earth on its own axis represents a day composed of a period of light followed by a period of darkness. For the regions of the Far East which were in the twilight position of the globe when the first day began, it

---

[1] See previous works by Louis JACOT.

was in the sixth revolution, that is on the sixth day, that Man appeared on the Earth. Is it possible that the author of Genesis, who claimed that Man was created on the sixth day, had a knowledge of geology? In any event, it is certain that Genesis corresponds, if not in its details at least in its broad lines, to evolution.

Geologists generally agree that there were four extensive glaciations during the Quaternary era, including the Günz which marked the beginning of the era. As the Quaternary is much shorter than the other eras, the repetition of four glaciations in so brief a period of time indicated that the Earth's rotation was gathering speed. This was perfectly in accord with general evolution as, with time, rotation, at first extremely slow, picks up speed until, as is the case today, it occurs in 24 hours.

As will be seen below (Section 10), the Earth's rotation did not pass abruptly from the millenial to the daily stage. There was a transition period during which it began to accelerate progressively, the glaciers alternately melting and refreezing. It would therefore be arbitrary to try to establish a fixed number of glaciations. If it is generally accepted that there were four, that is because the partial refreezings can be connected with the fourth. In the Alpine region, these various glaciations are called: Günz (the first, which links the Tertiary and Quaternary eras), Mindel (the most extensive), Riss (the third) and Würm (the most recent).

With the last glaciation, the prehistoric period of the Earth ends and the historic begins. The former therefore consisted of nine slow rotations extending from the Algonkian period to the Würm glaciation.

To summarize: it is obvious from careful study of climatic evolution in former ages that very cold periods, generally characterized by extensive glaciation, alternated with very hot periods during which inland seas evaporated and desert conditions were created. The cold periods corresponded to the midnight position on the globe and the hot periods to the midday. Between these two extremes were the dawn and twilight zones, certain areas of which, because of the inclination of the Earth's axis in relation to the plane of its orbit, passed alternately from light to darkness in the course of one translation of the Earth around the sun. As a result, these terrains are noteworthy for the alternation in their characteristic features. A close study of rock systems therefore makes it possible to establish the number of times that the Earth turned on its own axis during former ages and to reconstruct the conditions of existence of the flora and fauna of any given period.

6. *Immersions and emersions*

Another interesting fact established by geologists concerns the numerous advances and withdrawals of the sea. Extensive areas, almost entire continents, were periodically invaded by the sea and later emerged from the waters. This was a cyclic process that calls for explanation—an explanation, needless to say, that is related to glaciation phenomenon and slow rotation. When the ice, which was frequently more than 1,000 metres thick, moved into the light, the thaw inevitably raised the level of the surrounding seas. Every passage from darkness to light was therefore marked by a marine overflow. In the area situated at the midday position, on the contrary, continuous evaporation resulted in the drying up of inland seas and the formation of enormous deposits of salt and gypsum. At the twilight position, the rush of waters was not as great as at the dawn point, but nevertheless occurred because of the alternation of light and darkness due to the inclination of the Earth's axis. The climate was also very humid as the cooling down which necessarily occurred at this limit resulted in the condensation of the steam coming from the area in the midday position. The twilight region was therefore also subjected to marine overflows, less extensive however than those that occurred in the dawn area. They frequently took the form of flooding of the lagoons and consequent destruction of their fauna and flora. Finally, the face in darkness had a dry, cold climate that transformed the water into ice over vast areas.

In view of their positions in relation to the sun, the various longitudes did not all go through an Algonkian period or effect a complete first rotation up to the point at which they entered the night. On the other hand, in the Cambrian period, all moved out of darkness one after the other and all were subjected to considerable marine overflows. The chart of land and water masses at this period, as established by Furon [1], is particularly instructive. It shows the rising Arctic Ocean of the Cambrian period extending large channels towards the south until it linked up with the Mesogee sea which, at that time, completely surrounded the Earth at the equator. In Asia, west of Kolyma, the Arctic Ocean spread over a large part of the Siberian plateau and formed an extensive gulf in the area of Lake Baikal, rejoining, in the south, the waters bordering the Siberian shield. To the west, the Uralian Sea did the same, extending broadly southward to Persia and westward to Europe, which was entirely submerged except for a few islands, the two largest of which were Scandinavia and the Black Sea basin. Finally, in America, the Canadian shield was bounded by a large sea-arm east of Greenland while to the west a geosyncline covered the region now occupied by the Rocky Mountains and to the south the sea extended over the area of the Appalachians.

Having attained its maximum point in the Ordovician period, the marine overflow was replaced by a withdrawal, characterized by numerous alternations. A new rise in the Lower Devonian period, indicating a new passage from darkness to light, was followed in the mid- and Upper Devonian by a fall in sea level during which desert conditions, influencing vast continental areas, can be noted in the old red sandstone of the Eolian series of rocks. A new marine rise in the Lower Carboniferous period indicated that the rainy area at the twilight position had been reached.

[1] *Paléogéographie*, Payot, Paris.

Following the glaciation which interrupted this period, alternate rises and falls in sea level, which produced the coal deposits of the Stephanian epoch, indicated that the area of light had once again been reached.   The Permian period, the beginning of which corresponded to summer, was conspicuous for the emersion of extensive areas.   At the end of this period, the autumn (or twilight) position was reached and a large inland sea (the Zechstein) covered North Germany and England.   Then the cold resulted in the withdrawal of the waters.   The Russian sea arm disappeared altogether and an extensive continental area emerged in the north of Europe and the greater part of Siberia.   During the Lias epoch of the Triassic period, a new sea-rise indicated that an extensive glaciation had recently thawed, although it actually left very few traces.   The connections between the Arctic and Mesogee seas, which were still cut in the Triassic period, were then re-formed. Two large sea arms, one to the east of the Urals stretching as far as India, the other to the west of Scandinavia, crossing England and western Europe, reappeared[1].   The effect of the thaw was evident.

Then came the Jurassic period which marked the summer point, and here something surprising is to be observed.   As this period corresponded to the midday position, it should have been marked by a withdrawal of the waters and an increase in the continental areas, as in preceding rotations.   However, nothing of the kind occurred.   On the contrary, the Jurassic period, at least in Europe, was conspicuous for an extensive rise in the waters.   A withdrawal at the end of the Jurassic and the beginning of the Cretaceous was followed by numerous rises and falls during the entire Cretaceous period.   If land inundation was normal when a region reached the twilight position, and if it was also normal that it was replaced by emersion when cold and dryness occurred, the modifications in shorelines observable during the Cretaceous period were clearly abnormal.   What was particularly unusual was the

---

[1] FURON, *Paléogéographie*, Plate IX, the Lias.

extent of certain rises, such as that of the Upper Cretaceous. According to Moret[1]: "It was in the Upper Cretaceous period (Cenomanian epoch) that the Mediterranean flooded the heart of the African continent (which it had not done since the Primary era and was destined never to do again) and partly separated that continent from the American (Brazil), while the North Sea rose over England as far as Ireland and Scotland." These unusual rises were certainly due to an unusual occurrence. Reference will be made to this in the following section.

Finally, a definite withdrawal occurred in the Danian epoch at the end of the Cretaceous period. The fifth rotation had ended and with it the Secondary era.

A rise in the waters once again occurred at the beginning of the Tertiary era in the Eocene period. The sea advanced into the Paris basin and formed a shallow gulf extending more or less southwards. Its changing boundaries have been closely studied by geologists[2].

This rise continued during the Oligocene period in Belgium, Germany and the most widely separated points of the globe, finally giving place to a withdrawal at the end of this period, which corresponded to the midday position.

The waters rose once again in the Miocene period, which tallied with the twilight position, while in the Pliocene, which became colder and colder—the point at which night was reached—the sea withdrew from the greater part of Germany and Denmark. The Mediterranean which, in the Lower Miocene, had reached Switzerland and extended even as far as the Bavarian and Austrian plains, now considerably reduced its boundaries. Various orogenic phenomena took place at the time of this withdrawal. It was, in fact, at the end of the Miocene period that the Alpine plication occurred while its extension, in the form of Carpathians, took place in the

[1] *Précis de géologie*, p. 515.
[2] See diagram of these marine rises and falls on page 539 of the work by Moret just quoted.

Pliocene period.   As has already been explained, the formation of mountain chains did not occur at different dates in the east and in the west; on the contrary, plication was an abrupt and more or less simultaneous movement from one end of the chain to the other.   If the Carpathian plication seems to be of later formation, that is merely because this region, having moved into the night, was already in its Pliocene period, whereas the Swiss end, still in the light, was in its Miocene.

The entire Tertiary was an extremely disturbed era.   Not only did large plications occur but as early as the Lower Pliocene period, numerous volcanic formations appeared in the French Massif Central.

The sixth rotation of the Earth ended with this period.

In the Quaternary era, rotation began to speed up and the periods became shorter, though still long enough for extensive glacial caps to be formed.   The melting of each of these was followed by a rise in sea level during the inter-glacial period [1]. These rises and falls were not peculiar to the Quaternary but, as has just been seen, were repeated continuously throughout geological times.

Emile Haug, who made a detailed study of the advances and withdrawals of the sea, indicated that :

(1) the rises did not occur alternately in the northern and southern hemispheres but simultaneously in both;

(2) they were not confined to certain latitudes but were to be noted simultaneously in polar and equatorial regions;

(3) they were not world-wide.

The periodicity of these rises and the peculiarities, as noted by Haug, can only be acceptably explained in the context of the slow rotation of the Earth during former times.

---

[1] *La Terre s'en va* by Louis JACOT, Editions de la Table Ronde, Paris. The diagram reproduced in this publication by courtesy of Boule et Vallois (*Les Hommes fossiles*, Masson, Paris) shows the parallel between the glacial and inter-glacial periods on the one hand and the negative and positive movements of sea level on the other.   This will therefore not be repeated here.

7. *Expulsion of the moon*

The presence of a satellite revolving around the Earth poses a certain number of problems for anyone concerned about the world in which he lives. Newton tried to explain its movement by the "gravitation" exerted on it by our planet, a gravitation which was alleged to be "universal" and consequently responsible for causing the planets to turn around the sun. Now, as has already been demonstrated, this so-called universal gravitation is only found in manuals. It is easy to prove its non-existence not only in the world of the galaxies, which are withdrawing, but also in that of the atoms. The general laws of evolution—those of Hubble and of Bode—indicate that, on the contrary, planets are expelled by the sun and satellites by the planets. Any number of other facts—for example, the identity of elements, as ascertained by the spectrograph—have furthermore led the majority of physicists to conclude that the Earth was formerly part of the solar mass. The connection between planets and satellites, as has been seen, is a consequence of general expansion of the Universe and of rotation. The causes of expulsion and the manner in which it is effected will therefore not be repeated here. However, in view of the fact that an event of this kind could not have occurred on Earth without leaving traces on the terrestrial crust, the latter will now be studied in order to establish where the moon was situated before it was expelled from the Earth, and when this separation took place.

The common habit of believing that nothing ever happens any more but that everything was possible in the past as long as it was in a sufficiently distant past could lead to the assumption that the moon's expulsion took place at the beginning of the Earth's existence. But, as already explained, the phenomenon of expulsion is the result of rotation, and as our planet did not rotate on its own axis before the Primary era, the moon cannot have been expelled during the Archean age. The terrains of the later eras are, however, pretty well known and their stratification makes it possible to establish the orogenic movements that disturbed them. A geological examination of the globe leads to the conclusion that the moon was originally situated in the area now occupied by the Pacific Ocean and that it could not have been anywhere else. In fact, as expulsion is the result of rotation—that is, of a flattening at the poles and a swelling at the equator—it was from somewhere in this region that the mass had to come. In addition, it can be assumed that the tearing away of such a bulk must have led to the total disappearance of earlier geological strata over an extensive area, and in fact a study of ocean beds shows that the granite layer covering the globe as a whole above the basalt base rock disappeared in precisely the Pacific area, leaving the basalt exposed [1].

Numerous eminent paleontologists affirm that a continent occupied the region of the Pacific, at least up to the Triassic period of the Secondary era. This is not a new theory. Even in the last century, Suess, on the basis of remarkable studies, demonstrated the existence of land connections between the Indian peninsula, South Africa and Australia up to the end of the Triassic. He concluded that a large continent, to which he gave the name "Gondwana", had existed in the Pacific zone. In view of the fact that his arguments were well founded, the majority of geologists and paleontologists rallied to his point of view. Others, however, were led to refute this theory, not by challenging Suess' arguments as such, but by insisting on the physical impossibility for so vast a continent to have sunk to so great a depth. For this to have happened, they said, the Earth would have had to be hollow, which was an absurdity.

There is nothing inconceivable in the suggestion that a mass corresponding to that of the moon could formerly have been situated in the Pacific zone. The moon's volume is approximately

---

[1] GAMOW, *Biographie de la Terre.*

20 milliard kms³ ; the Pacific ocean measures from 160 to 180 million km², depending on the boundaries which are assigned to it. Even if Gondwana is assumed to have had a surface area appreciably smaller than this—that is about 100 million km² or two-thirds of its northern counterpart—the hump produced by the flattening of the globe must have been about 200 kilometres high. Now, as the present diameter of the Earth is 43 kilometres greater at the equator than between the poles, a hump about 200 kilometres in height is in fact not excessive.

The idea that the moon must formely have occupied the Pacific area has already been put forward by various persons, in particular Sir George Howard Darwin, the English scientist. However, his claim that its separation occurred far back in the night of the world is in contradiction to geological facts that prove the existence of a continent in this region up to the Secondary era.

The Pacific is the deepest ocean in the world. Marine depths of 8,000 and 10,000 metres and more have been located not only in the proximity of Japan but also of America.

The situation can be summarized as follows : the expulsion of the moon could not have taken place before the Earth began to turn on its own axis. On the other hand, it has been established that a continent called Gondwana still occupied the Pacific zone at the beginning of the Secondary era. The moon's expulsion must therefore have occurred subsequently, that is, either at the end of the Secondary or at the beginning of the Tertiary.

The big marine rise of the Jurassic period in Europe followed by an even higher rise in the Cenomanian epoch of the Cretaceous seem to have heralded the event, and in fact the expansion that was taking place in the region of Gondwana must have caused the seas to flow into other areas.

An event as important as the expulsion of a satellite cannot occur without being accompanied and followed by unusual orogenic movements, and this is exactly what can be noted in the Tertiary era which was the most disturbed of all the eras in the

history of the Earth.   The large plications extending from the
Alps to the Himalayas occurred at this time, and although there
was nothing new about the formation of mountain chains, the
Tertiary was conspicuous for even more far-reaching events than
those that had occurred in earlier periods and for which the only
explanation can be the expulsion of the moon.   We shall now
study these events more closely.

8. *Drift of continents*

Just as Suess, by his comparative study of fauna and flora, had
been led to the conclusion that a continent had existed in the
Pacific area, so Wegener, comparing the coastlines of the Atlantic,
noticed that they corresponded, Brazil fitting perfectly into the
Gulf of Guinea.   Astonishing similarities in strata had already
been noted in the coastlines bordering both sides of the Atlantic.
In addition, it seemed probable that early European and American
plications had formerly formed a continuous chain.   Finally,
numerous paleontological facts indicated a close relationship between the two coastlines today separated by several thousand kilometres.   Amongst these facts should be quoted the extensive areas
over which the garden snails, earthworms, pearl oysters, conifers,
heather, etc., spread.

Examining closely all these data, Wegener arrived at the
conclusion that America had been joined to Africa and Europe up
to the Cretaceous period and that it was at this particular period
that the continents began to separate, drifting like rafts.   He
studied the successive stages of this dislocation, noted that other
regions had also drifted, and undertook to reconstruct the globe
at different periods (Plate 12).   His book on this subject [1] is one
of the most interesting of the century.

[1] WEGENER, *La Genèse des continents et des océans.*

While Wegener's theory was very sound as far as the facts were concerned—extension of mountain chains, spread of glaciations, similarity of strata, deposits, flora, fauna, etc.—its weakness lay in the difficulty he had in explaining the cause of the movements. These were even more astonishing in that, up to the Cretaceous period, nothing of the kind had ever been recorded. In fact, at that time, the surface of the globe consisted of two large continental areas separated by the Mesogee sea which surrounded the Earth at the equator. Each of these large continents was periodically invaded by the waters produced by the melting of the ice and forming more or less deep channels reaching sometimes as far as the Mesogee itself. One of these arms was formed periodically along the Urals, another between Europe and America which, at that period, constituted a single continental block. The northern continent accordingly consisted of Asia, Europe, and North America. The southern (Gondwana) continent was formed by Australia, Africa, South America and vast territories occupying what is now the Pacific area. Now why did continents that had remained in the same position for thousands of years suddenly begin to drift?

The expulsion of the moon once again supplies the answer. At the moment of its separation, a deep pit was created at the point of rupture and into this the seas poured. However, as the density of sea water is three times less than that of rock, balance could not be restored. This extensive southern pit opposite the northern continental shelf did not supply the necessary counter-weight and, as a result, the Earth's axis was disturbed and rotation "limped" along. Furthermore, the continents had, until then, mutually supported one another by virtue of their substructure. When the pit was formed, this fundamental support was undermined and all the neighbouring parts of the Earth's crust began to slip in the direction of the cavity. This movement towards the Pacific pit has not escaped the attention of geologists who have indicated it on various charts, such as that drawn up by Taylor (see Plate 13) [1]. Another vivid chart is that of the subterranean earthquakes and ocean deeps of the Pacific, drawn up by Goguel (see Plate 14) [2]. These displacements did not occur without disturbances; in fact the latter have lasted even up to the present day and are still manifest in the form of the earthquakes and volcanic eruptions occurring at the periphery of the Pacific pit.

The large Asiatic shelf did not escape the effects of this generalized flow of the under-lying strata in the direction of the cavity and its entire eastern edge collapsed. Seas bordered by chains of islands up to Kamchatka testify to this subsidence. All southeast Asia was subjected to a vast twisting movement southwards. This is particularly visible in Indochina where the big plication which extended the Himalaya chain eastward suddenly makes a turn and drops towards the sea where it is lost beneath the waves. From this strung-out formation nothing emerges but the peaks forming the Polynesian Islands.

To the south, the Australian block, including New Zealand, separated itself from India and Africa and slipped eastward. It penetrated and became intermingled with the islands of Oceania with which, until then, it had in no way been connected, to which fact earlier flora and fauna bear witness.

When the Asiatic block shifted towards the south, its path was barred by the Indian peninsula (which formerly formed the northern part of the continent of Gondwana, the major part of which had been expelled); consequently all the northern part of India became covered by the vast Himalayan plication that occurred in the Tertiary era. To Argand [3] all credit is due for having recognized and explained this fantastic overlapping of Tibet on the Hindu remains of the continent of Gondwana.

The drag towards the Pacific pit was felt still further afield. As the Earth is spherical, the slipping of the strata adjacent to the

[1] *Bull. Geol. Soc. of America*, T. 21, June 1910.
[2] *Traité de tectonique*, p. 80, Masson.
[3] ARGAND, *Tectonique de l'Asie*.

pit occurred as much in the west as in the east.   The continental block formed by Africa and America was drawn in opposite directions and finally split apart.   An enormous "S" began to form from south to north and separated not only Africa from America but also America from Europe, to which it had up till then been joined.   The two separate parts drifted apart and the big "S" widened still further to become the Atlantic Ocean.   America drifted towards the west, Eurasia and Africa in the opposite direction, while Madagascar, having had a head-start, separated itself from Africa and drifted increasingly far away.

For a long time after that, Africa was still being tugged in opposite directions, as testified by the large fractures that were created subsequently in the Tertiary and Quaternary eras.   The waters of the great equatorial lakes poured into one of these fractures to form the Nile, the longest river in the world, exceeding 6,000 kilometres.   This fracture was extended northward in the form of the trench now occupied by the Dead Sea, situated 400 metres below sea level and thereby constituting the lowest region of the globe.   The tugging forces have not yet ceased and violent earthquakes still occur today as part of their extension into Asia Minor and even as far as the Caucasus and Iran.

This drift produced not only fractures but also trenches due to subsidence (the most important being that of the Red Sea which had not existed previously) and rocking motions of the ground with accompanying breaks in level.   As a result of the eastward trend, the eastern side of Lake Albert is now at a mean altitude of only 500 metres whereas the western side is at 2,500 metres.   The difference between the two sides of Lake Tanganyika is 800 metres (3,300 in the west and 2,500 in the east).   The pull towards the Pacific pit was therefore definitely much stronger eastward than towards the west in the direction of the Atlantic.   These changes in level produced a reversal in the flow of the waters of Lakes Victoria and Kyoga.   Up to the Pleistocene period of the Quaternary era, the Kafue river and its tributaries formed a dentritic

network flowing westwards. The Katonga river similarly evacuated the waters of Lake Victoria towards the west. Then, as a
result of the rocking motions mentioned above, the Kafue and
Katonga changed direction and both now flow eastward [1].

A study of a chart of the Atlantic bed reveals the surprising
fact that it is divided in its entire length from north to south into
two more or less equal parts by a long submarine ridge in the
form of an "S". This can be seen very clearly in a chart drawn
up by Daly [2]. It is therefore quite natural to suppose that this
long ridge marks the point where these two blocks separated, the
American drifting towards the west, the European and African
towards the east. This conclusion is confirmed by a study of
seismic centres and volcanoes. Whereas those of the Pacific are
so densely packed around the circumference of the ocean that
they form what has been called the Pacific belt of fire, their distribution is quite different in the Atlantic. The existence of such
earthquake centres along the coast indicates that the displacement
of these two blocks has still not ended—the recent disaster at
Agadir is a reminder of the fact—but the most unstable area is to
be found along the median ridge of the Atlantic bed, which is
perfectly logical if this is, in fact, the line of demarcation between
the respective eastward and westward drifts [3].

The southward trend of the entire eastern coastline of continental Asia, the twist in the Himalayan range in Indochina, and its
subsequent submersion, the overlapping of India by Tibet, the
separation of America from Europe and Africa to which it was

[1] HOLMES, *Principles of Geology*.

[2] In *Architecture of the earth*, D. Appleton Century Company, New York.
This chart was reproduced as Figure 96 in *La Terre s'en va*, by Louis JACOT,
Editions de la Table Ronde, Paris.

[3] See chart of volcanoes and seismic centres of the Atlantic drawn up by
Goguel, *Traité de Tectonique*, Masson, Paris. A comparison between this and
the chart of volcanoes and seismic centres of Japan drawn up by Gutenberg
and Richter is very revealing. In the latter case, the deep centres are very
close to the continent. These two charts were reproduced in *La Terre s'en va*,
by Louis JACOT, Editions de la Table Ronde, Paris.

formerly joined, the large African faults—were not all these gigantic upheavals an indication of a general displacement towards the Pacific pit and do they not prove that an even more violent upheaval had occurred there—in other words, the expulsion of the continent of Gondwana, which became the moon?

This event can be situated, in time, between two extreme dates. The uniformity of flora in the Triassic period indicates that the continent of Gondwana still existed at that time. The continuance of this uniformity into the Jurassic period is confirmed by the presence of a heather (Thinnfeldia Odontopteroide) that grew abundantly in the Cape, India, Australia and South America [1].

According to Wegener [2], the division of the block formed by South America and Africa took place in the Cretaceous period of the Secondary era whereas that of Europe and North America followed a little later in the early Tertiary.

This being the case, we are led to the conclusion that Gondwana, still present during the Jurassic period, was expelled at the end of the Cretaceous, the dislocation of the continents being a direct consequence of the void created in the Pacific area by this event. Africa, it must be remembered, was still in the Cretaceous when Asia, which preceded it in the rotation of the Earth, had already entered the Tertiary era.

The expulsion of the moon can consequently be established as having occurred either at the end of the Secondary era or at the beginning of the Tertiary, depending on which of the geological calendars—the occidental or the oriental—is used.

Wegener's theory, which was very popular and received the support of the majority of the most eminent geologists of the 1920's and '30's is now somewhat discredited. The two main criticisms raised against it are: 1. it does not explain the *cause* of the widespread continental movements and 2. no reason is given for the fact that such movements did not take place prior to the Tertiary

[1] GIGNOUX, *Géologie stratigraphique*, p. 419.
[2] See page 17 of work already referred to.

era, nor for the fact that today they are almost imperceptible. However, if the evolution of our planet is considered in the context of universal evolution and followed carefully through the ages. Wegener's theory will prove to be entirely acceptable. The upheaval caused by the expulsion of a satellite by the Earth was responsible for the shifting of the continents during the Cretaceous period, even though no such thing had ever taken place before. It also explains clearly why the American continent, having struck up against the Asiatic in the Kamchatka area in the north, has now reached the end of its run and is no longer subject to the same movement as before. Volcanic activity around the Pacific, however, indicates that this general displacement is not yet completely terminated.

9. Formation of mountain chains

The formation of mountain chains cannot adequately be explained except in the context of evolution. For a long time it was attributed to the contraction of the terrestrial globe, subsequent to a cooling process. The Earth was compared to an apple which becomes wrinkled in the cellar during winter. Later it was realized that neither the positions of the mountains on the surface of the globe nor their structure—the majority of them showed that they had been created through the effect of horizontal thrust—corresponded to this picture and this theory. From a study of extensive overthrust along the edges of the Alps, Schardt assumed that they were produced by the flow of the surface layer of the Earth's crust over an inclined plane. This explanation, which can, of course, apply to certain terrains, in fact merely shifts the problem, as it then becomes necessary to explain why the plane should have been inclined. The isostasy theory is based on the assumption that the densest part of the globe forms depressions and the less dense, projections. As erosion constantly upsets this balance by lightening the prominences and overloading the depressions, the latter form folds, rising from the sea-bed and encroaching on the land areas. This theory, however, does not correspond to the position of the chains which were formed through the ages. As to the "mobilers", they explain the folding of the continental shelves by the resistance they encountered in the substructure as they drifted. This theory tallies with a number of facts but cannot be generally applied, as chains of mountains had been formed prior to the displacement of the continents. The most widely held at the moment is the convection-current theory which returns in part to that of the wrinkled apple but includes the principle that there are currents of different temperatures under the Earth's crust. Here again, however, the theory is inacceptable : when differences in temperature are small, nothing happens as excess heat is easily diffused by degrees ; when the differences are great and transmission difficult, then the well-known phenomenon of the volcano occurs. But the majority of mountain chains are not volcanic in origin.

The existence of active volcanoes can be misleading. Many mountains are of course of eruptive origin, that is, were produced by a vertical upheaval due to the expansion force of enclosed gases (very often steam) ; but there are others (and this applies to the chains) that are formed neither of lava nor of ash and have absolutely nothing to do with volcanism. In fact, instead of being the result of vertical upheaval, they were formed by folds (that is, by a horizontal movement) the general structure of which can be reconstructed thanks to their normally very well preserved strata.

Even from a bird's-eye view, the profile of the folds is particularly visible in the Jura mountains, for example. They can be followed, each one separately and parallel, for considerable distances, as erosion has scarcely modified the original relief, the altitude throughout being relatively low. In the Alps, on the contrary, where the altitude is appreciably higher, erosion has transformed the original folds from top to bottom. Nevertheless, a systematic study of strata has enabled geologists to reconstruct the original position of the terrain.   According to Argand, the Dent-Blanche group, with the Cervin, was ripped out of its substratum south-east of Mont-Rose and transported over the latter for about 40 kilometres on the St. Bernard surface layer, with which it previously had had no connection.   The Swiss groups and the fore-Alps apparently effected an even longer run as their point of departure was much further to the south-east and their point of arrival more than 60 kilometres to the north-west.   They accordingly moved a distance in excess of 100 kilometres.   This lateral movement makes it quite clear that the origin of these chains of mountains was a tangential thrust and not a vertical upheaval.

As the existence of mountain chains is as certain as that of the moon, a suitable explanation must be found for these formations. However, an explanation can only be considered suitable if it takes into consideration both the extent of the phenomenon, its repetition through the ages, the position of the chains and the way in which they were formed.   It should also explain why there is a fundamental difference between the relief of the moon— where no mountain chains can be seen—and that of the Earth where the large chains predominate.

If the formation of mountain chains is placed in the context of the general evolution of the planet as now understood, there is no longer anything mysterious about these plications or their repetition through the ages.

Several chains, now completely worn away, existed prior to the present ones.   They have, however, been identified, both in position and age, through the upheavals they created in the ground. The earliest chain, called the Huronian (in the Algonkian period), completely surrounded the Earth near the North Pole.   The next in chronological order, called the Caledonian (in the Devonian period) is parallel to and to the south of the first.   The third, Hercynian (in the Carboniferous period) is also parallel to the first two and still further to the south. The same applies to the fourth, the Alpine and Himalayan chains of the Tertiary era. The connection between the formation of these chains and the rotation of the Earth is obvious. Marcel Bertrand wrote on the subject [1]:

"In spite of wide irregularities in their contours, the four chains testify to a general sequence in the deformation process around the pole; whether unbroken or not, they define four circumpolar areas and represent the four chapters in the history of the globe... But the arrangement of the chains, such as it is known, suffices to call to mind, in spite of the absence of any geometric pattern, a connection with rotation and the flattening of the globe."

All spherical masses are flattened through the effect of rotation. In the case of the Earth, this rotation, as has been seen, began in the Algonkian period and it was at that time that the first chains were formed. As the flattening process increased, that is, with each turn, another chain was formed, farther south than the previous one. Consequently, each plication of the northern hemisphere was closer to the equator than the preceding one. As this is in harmony with evolution, it is understandable that these successive compressions of the globe finally resulted in the expulsion of a satellite.

The account of the history of the Earth given in Section 11, below, shows that the plication always took place in the area situated on the dark side of the globe. It can therefore be assumed that the weight of the glacial caps played a significant part in the formation of folds.

As rotation is the primary cause for the existence of mountain chains, it is easy to explain why the moon, which always turns the

[1] *Œuvres géologiques*, I, p. 18, Paris, 1927.

same face towards the Earth and consequently does not rotate on its own axis, is without plication.

The Earth's rotation is not, however, the direct cause of all mountain chain formation, as indicated by those which are not parallel to the equator. But in their case it can be said that it is the indirect cause as it resulted in the expulsion of a satellite and the consequent drift of the continents. Now, clearly, as pointed out with good reason by the supporters of the theory of continental displacement, the dislocation and the drift itself did not occur without friction. The continents were not equipped with ball-bearings and, when shifting, they encountered resistance. This produced folds that always formed in the prow of these immense "rafts", never at the stern. This is particularly noticeable in the case of the large Andes and Rocky Mountain chains which rise up from one end to the other of the American continent, forward of its movement westward.

There are consequently two different processes at the root of mountain chain formation and these can be recognized by the structure of the folds. The chains caused by the resistance encountered during the drift of the continents are, like the Rockies, fan-shaped : front and back are formed of folds fanning over one another while the flattened median part has scarcely moved at all and only from bottom to top, the displacement having been small and having taken place in a horizontal direction. On the contrary, the folds formed by the flattening of the terrestrial globe, such as the Alps, lie one on top of the other and are transported horizontally for considerable distances.

Whatever the cause, it is obvious that plications, like earthquakes, are extremely abrupt and rapid movements. If certain geologists believe and have written that these formations occur very slowly, this, as already explained, is because they have noted that the mountain chains parallel to the equator were formed earlier in the west than in the east. They have naturally assumed that the chain took thousands of years to form. This error stems from a misunderstanding regarding the geological periods, their order of succession being valid only for given regions in different longitudes. For example, the Triassic period, that is, the dawn position for one region, is concurrent with the Jurassic of its eastern neighbour, which is already at the midday point, and with the Cretaceous for the zone situated still further to the east that has now been carried into the twilight position by the Earth's slow rotation. Plication is in fact more or less simultaneous from one end to the other. Moreover, in his treatise on tectonics, Goguel said : "These differences in age according to position should not obscure the basic unity of the large orogenic structures." A little reflection on the mechanism of these plications, in the course of which enormous masses were transported over others, will make it clear that such bulks cannot have remained "suspended" for thousands of years and that if plications had occurred slowly they could never have imprisoned the unbelievable quantities of vegetable and animal matter that form the basis of oil fields.

The majority of mountain chains have risen from the bed of the sea—yet another mystery to be solved. In the globe's flattening process, the sea areas obviously constituted the weaker part of the Earth's crust as water has neither the cohesion nor the density of rock. Furthermore, terrains formed by underwater sedimentation are more pliant than the old, solidified rocks of the continents. In the flattening process, the areas under water, being less resistent than the continental shelves surrounding them, naturally gave way and folded under tangential pressure.

Repeated glaciations, rises and falls in sea level, climates quite different from those of the present day, drift of continents, formation of mountain chains, all these phenomena are part of a whole. It is useless to try to explain each by a separate theory, as all are the result of evolution and understandable only in that context.

10. Quickened rotation: the Deluge

Formerly, one rotation of the Earth lasted thousands of years. Today, it takes place in 24 hours. It is not reasonable to suppose that such a change occurred without a period of transition.

In fact, the Quaternary era, which is the shortest in the history of the Earth—as confirmed by the thinness of its deposits—was marked by four glaciations, if the one that separates it from the Tertiary (the Günz glaciation) is counted. Terrestrial rotation was therefore picking up speed. However, the thickness of the glacial formations of this period indicates that one revolution still lasted a very long time. Such men as were then living were obliged to remain in the zones between light and darkness; subsequent slow rotation necessitated migration and raised tragic problems for the human species of the period.

Then rotation picked up speed considerably. The glaciers which melted during the period of light were only partially reformed during the period of darkness, with the result that thaws and subsequent inundations became more and more frequent. Each rotation, at first longer than a year, became shorter, with the result that seasonal changes were finally produced, as today, by the inclination of the Earth's axis and no longer corresponded to the periods of melting and refreezing resulting from rotation. The rise of the waters was accordingly very unequal, depending on whether the ice moved into the light at the summer or winter solstice. There must have been spectacular floodings.

In countries favoured by conditions—in India, Mesopotamia, along the Nile, the Danube, etc.—men came out of their caves in increasing numbers and constructed shelters, huts or pile dwellings. They formed groups in villages or towns, domesticated animals and cultivated plants, cereals, materials for weaving, etc. The stone used by man at this period was not only chipped but polished. Later, metal industries appeared as well as pottery and materials. Copper was known in Egypt five thousand years before the

Christian era and became widely used in the fourth millenium. The magnificent golden objects discovered in the royal tombs at Ur, in Chaldea, as well as the rich pottery manufactured in China, India, the Eastern Mediterranean, South Russia, Roumania, Bohemia, etc., also date from this period. In short, industry and the arts were developing rapidly and real centres of civilization were being created. Man had entered the historic period.

When did this period of transition between the slow rotation, that took thousands of years to complete, and rotation as is known today, come to an end? In other words, since when has the Earth been turning on its own axis in about 24 hours? To answer this question we must take into account the fact that acceleration of rotation naturally had consequences that were in some cases temporary, in others lasting. Amongst the latter was the stabilization of climates as known today, or more precisely their differences according to latitude. This stabilization allowed man to spread out over the globe. But the most important of the immediate consequences must certainly have been the extremely rapid melting of the remaining glacial formations, daily rotation to all intents and purposes preventing nocturnal refreezing, in spring as much as in summer and in autumn, over the greater part of the globe. The event which occurred after Man's appearance on the Earth and in which he participated—the Deluge—can be dated with a certain precision partly through the traces it left in the terrain, partly through the records left by witnesses.

The total melting of enormous caps of ice covering regions that are today temperate was not a new phenomenon. It occurred at each rotation, when the ice moved into the area of light and caused vast rises in sea level. As Man had already appeared on the Earth and had experienced four glaciations, he had consequently been exposed to four great floods. Now, as will be seen later, the memory of these catastrophies passed from generation to generation. The last flood, however, had a particular character of its own as it marked the end of a certain climatic condition and the beginning of an altogether different one.   From then on, the speed of rotation resulted in a much more rapid melting of the ice and was responsible for its catastrophic proportions.

Sir Leonard Wooley, when excavating at Ur in Chaldea where he discovered remains of remarkable civilizations, became aware of the fact that, having reached a certain level, his workers had struck a layer of absolutely barren clay.   He was about to call off operations when he realized that the level of the ground was still too high in relation to that of the delta.   Work therefore continued. Then, beneath a 2.5-metre thickness of alluvium that contained nothing at all, the workers suddenly discovered the remains of civilizations quite different from the others.   A layer of clay of such thickness denotes an exceptional flood.   On the basis of what seemed to be very reliable archeological data, Sir Leonard established the date of this incident as being around 3,500 B. C., that is, at the same geological period as the flood mentioned in the Bible, which is alleged to have occurred in the year 3,852 B. C. The discrepancy between the two dates is minimal, in fact even non-existent, as will be shown later in connection with the calendar.

The Deluge is consequently not a legend, as is still often thought ; it is an historic incident that can be dated with a certain accuracy and was the result of the melting of the ice, subsequent to the speeding up of the Earth's rotation.

Between the last glaciation of the Quaternary era and the Deluge there was accordingly a transition period in the speed of rotation, which was faster than it had been during former periods but was nevertheless slower than it is today.   This period was very short.   Professor de Geer, who has studied the varve cha- racteristic of the seasons that succeeded each other from the time of the melting of the Scandinavian glaciers to the present day, finds that they number 14,000.   If 5,500, representing approxi- mately the number of years elapsed since the Deluge, are subtracted from the total of 14,000 only 8,500 are left to cover the lapse of time between the last glaciation and the Deluge.   And even these

8,500 varva do not represent 8,500 years, as might be supposed from hasty conclusions, but a maximum of 1,500. The reasons are simple.

If an attempt is made to imagine what must have been the calendar before the Deluge, it will be realized that the succession of seasons (which now occurs in the course of one year) was primarily the result of the speeding up of rotation that produced the alternations of light and darkness. Now if the chronology found in ancient texts is studied, that of the Bible in particular, a fundamental difference will be observed in the manner of calculating the ages before and after the Deluge. Antediluvian ages are everywhere much longer than the postdiluvian, and this to an extraordinary extent. The cause of this difference is not, as is still being taught today, the morbid tendency of all historians to exaggerate, but the use of a time unit shorter than our year. This unit was simply the Earth's rotation, an obvious unit for that period, as it was rotation that regulated all human life. This unit of measure, that decreased with the acceleration of rotation can be calculated as having been about two months. It represented the antediluvian "year". Reduced by five-sixths, the ages of the patriarchs now become reasonable. The striking anomaly between the age at which Noah was supposed to have had his first son (500 years) and the parallel age that applied from the time of Adam—it varied between 65 and a maximum of 187 years —can be explained by the confusion that reigned in the ways of counting the periods that were inevitably changing with the change in the rhythm of the climates. For a certain time, calculations continued to be made on the basis of terrestrial rotation, days thus being added to the basic 2-month period. The figures were obviously rounded off for Noah (first child at the age of 500 and the Deluge at 600) and reveal the inaccuracy resulting from the change. This inaccuracy continued to be reflected in the ages of Noah's first descendants, who still lived for as much as 400 years. After the Deluge, the age of the patriarchs dropped immediately from 900 to 400, then to 200 years and children were born in their father's thirtieth year. There were clearly two ways of calculating the years before and after the Deluge.

This difference in ages before and after is not peculiar to the Bible. It is the despair of all archeologists who have excavated sites dating back before the Deluge. It is found on all the Mesopotamian tablets giving the dynastic lists of Erech, Kish, etc., and again in the list supplied by Berossus of the kings of Babylonia. The mystery is only cleared up if the data furnished by records are related to prevailing conditions in the Earth's rotation and translation.

It can therefore reasonably be concluded that the climatic differences resulting from rotation were reflected in the terrains and that the 8,500 varva noted by de Geer for that period actually represent only about 1,500 (not 8,500) years.

This argument, it must be emphasized, is not in the nature of an attempt to fabricate fantastic theories regarding all sorts of legends. The opposite is the case. A study of evolution will show that terrestrial rotation was modified through the ages. Very slow up to the end of the Quaternary era, it became daily at the time of the Deluge. This has been established by all the phenomena reviewed up to this point (glaciation, rise and fall of sea level, periodic change in climate, etc.). This being the case, the problem consists merely in explicitly defining the conditions in which this acceleration in terrestrial rotation took place. As Man was already witness to these events, there is nothing unreasonable in supposing that he might have retained certain recollections of them.

A study of ancient texts and legends in fact reveals that they contain much more truth than is generally imagined. For a long time, the Iliad was considered to be a fantasy poem about a more or less imaginary battle, but by following closely Homer's text, Schliemann succeeded in locating the exact site of Troy and, after carrying out systematic excavations, uncovered its ruins.

Numerous ancient texts can constitute documents of the highest value regarding the conditions of humanity in early ages, with the proviso that the trouble be taken to study them correctly. This is the case with the story that Plato recounts in Timaeus about the destruction of Atlantis, a continent situated beyond Gibraltar. What has been learnt from Wegener regarding the displacement of the continents and the rift that occurred between Europe and Africa on the one hand and America on the other makes it very probable that extensive areas did sink out of sight as a result of this rupture.

In Critias, the priest from Sais who visited Solon told him that Greece had been subjected to four floods in the course of the previous millenium, whereas Egypt had been saved thanks to the special rhythm of the Nile. Stories about the Deluge are found amongst a large number of races and, curiously, many of them speak of four successive floods separated by long periods of drought. This has already been dealt with [1] and will not be discussed again here. Suffice it to note that if the Egyptian priest speaks of four floods, if Oannes went four times to civilize Mesopotamia, if the Aztecs record four periods of sudden death and the Mayas four successive suns, this is quite easy to accept as, after Man's appearance on the Earth, there were four slow rotations accompanied by four successive glaciations, four resulting floods, four periods of intense drought and four slow disappearances of the sun below the horizon. The Mayas claim that the sun was devoured by jaguars. Surely this can be regarded as a highly imaginative picture of a luminary which, having shone brightly for a very long time, little by little sinks below the horizon !

11. Age of the Earth

I : General considerations

The many preconceived ideas that are held on this subject make it a very ticklish one to deal with. Erroneous and widespread

---

[1] *La Terre s'en va*, by Louis JACOT, Editions de la Table Ronde, Paris.

assumptions in this connection are so firmly anchored that it is almost impossible to eradicate them.

And the first serious misunderstanding to be cleared up is the question of what is meant by the age of the Earth. The Earth was formed from universal matter which is the same everywehre and has the same age everywhere, as far as it is possible for the word "age" to have a meaning when applied to an eternal substance. This term, in fact, can only have significance in this context if related to a given event.

But it immediately becomes evident that there will not be agreement between scientists regarding the age of the Earth until they are in agreement regarding this given event from which it is to be calculated ; and even then, it is not enough to say that this should be, for example, the moment at which the Earth became an independent entity because, at that point, yet another agreement has to be reached : was the globe ejected just as it is from the sun or was it the result of the condensation of a nebula, or did it simply come from "space", being one fine day captured by the sun ?

By not recognizing the general lines of evolution, many scientists have completely distorted the problem of the Earth's age, claiming to have attained rigorous precision on the basis of certain specific phenomena. In fact, these phenomena can only be of significance if interpreted correctly, in the general context of the evolutionary process. This is paramount.

And this is precisely what is lacking in the method based on radioactivity. As is known, radioactivity is a process in which certain bodies said to be radioactive, such as uranium, actinium, thorium, are transmuted in such fashion as to become lead isotopes following the emission of helium. Having established that a mass of uranium produces, each year, the same proportion of helium and lead (1.5 ten-millionth of its mass) whatever the conditions of pressure and temperature, various scientists decided to calculate the age of the rocks, which almost all contain radioactive bodies, by determining their proportions of uranium, lead and helium.

The greater the proportion of lead the longer the duration of radio-activity and consequently the older the rock. The following figures have been put forward : the Archean age was supposed to have lasted at least a milliard years, the Primary era, 300 million, the Secondary, 150 million, the Tertiary and Quaternary (combined) 50 million (10,000 years only for the latter) ; that is a total of 1.5 milliard. This figure was considered for many years to repre-sent the exact age of the Earth. However, certain scientists decided to scrutinise the analyses and calculations more carefully and, in the measure that new and improved methods were used, the figures increased in proportion. From 1.5 milliard, the figure went up to 2, then 3, then 5, then 10, and today various writers have established the age of the Earth as being 15 milliard years ! Such differences are clearly no recommendation for methods that are supposed to be absolutely accurate.

The calculations are in fact incorrect because they are based on two fundamental errors. The first is the assumption that radioactivity has necessarily always been the same through the ages. But the example of the sun, where this phenomenon is of an extreme intensity, proves the contrary. As the Earth originally formed part of the sun and is moving away from it progressively, it is certain that radioactivity has not been constant on our planet. The second error is the assumption that the ore only began to disintegrate from the moment it was incorporated in the rock, but nothing—absolutely nothing—supports this claim. Radioactivity is a phenomenon caused by the evolution of the Universe (Chapter Seven, Section 5). It has affected the Earth not only since its formation but even prior to that time, when it formed part of the solar mass. The residual quantity of lead is therefore not a determining factor. As to the assumption regarding the expelled helium, this is equally open to doubt. Helium is an extremely light gas. It is therefore incautious to pretend that the quantity found in a rock necessarily represents the production of radio-active elements of that rock since its formation, that nothing has been lost, and that nothing has been added from elsewhere. Sedimentary layers resulting from erosion are generally carried into depressions by water. They are therefore not constituted of new material. On the contrary, all their constituent elements have a very long history, during which they were not able to escape the effects of radioactivity. The method based on the radioactive state of rocks is therefore very unsound. It is all the more dangerous in that, being founded on an undeniable phenomenon and on rigorous mathematical calculations, it is considered to be "strictly scientific".

And yet it is clear that the results of this method are quite untenable since they are in flagrant contradiction to the general law of evolution—Hubble's law. According to this, the galaxies are annually moving away from one another in a proportion of about ½ milliardth of the distance that separates them. Consequently, if this proportion is applied back through the ages, it leads inevitably to the conclusion that 2 milliard years ago the Universe would have had a radius that was nearly zero. Now, even if, by transposing Bode's law to the galactic systems, it were considered that the Universe expands progressively and that this expansion was accordingly less in the past, there can still be no question, in view of the absurdity of a Universe with a zero radius and the necessity of stopping somewhere in the backward calculation of time, of the age of the Universe being established at figures way above 2 milliard years.

Now, as the sun is a product of the galaxy, the time from which it existed as an entity must be appreciably less than the galactic age. If it is now considered that the sun, which occupies an eccentric position in the heart of the galactic vortex, certainly took considerable time to reach this point, that a very great portion of its existence passed before it began to turn on its own axis and expel planets, that before the creation of the Earth it had already expelled Mars, the Asteroids, Jupiter, Saturn, Uranus, Neptune and Pluto as well as all the celestial bodies still further off, the debris of which is seen in the form of comets, the age of our Earth cannot be more than a minute fraction of that of the sun. There is therefore no question of milliards of years.

It is in a completely unbiased frame of mind and ignoring the results reached by the experts on radioactivity that the problem of the Earth's "age" should be considered and solved. This age should be regarded as being the period of time that has elapsed from the time of the Earth's expulsion by the sun to the present day.

II : Earth's age in the context of evolution

The salient facts in the evolution of the solar system are the periodic expulsion of planets by the sun and their progressive movement away from it. It is therefore the evolution in translation—that is, in the successive orbits described by the Earth around the sun—that must now be examined in the same way that terrestrial rotation was studied. In a Universe in which everything evolves, there is no motion so favoured as to escape this general phenomenon, and in the course of ages, evolution necessarily affects the translation as much as the rotation of the celestial bodies.

But how is evolution in translation shown? As all the planets are moving away from the sun in accordance with Bode's law, there is of course no such thing as a closed planetary orbit. On the contrary, each orbit was, is and always will be larger than the preceding one. The Earth therefore does not describe ellipses around the sun but spirals.

As each orbit is always larger than the previous one, and as the velocity of the Earth on its orbit is known (30 km/sec), the simplest way of finding out the increase in distance would seem to be by comparing the times taken to complete two successive orbits. Unfortunately, Man has taken the Earth's translation around the sun—that is to say, the year—as his time-standard, based on the assumption that the planet always takes the same time to describe its circuit. Clocks were set on this basis. But in such circumstances, two successive paths clearly cannot result in two different times. It is therefore necessary to fall back on other methods.

The first thing to be done is to examine closely what is meant by the word : year, that is, one turn of the Earth around the sun. And a surprising fact is immediately noticed. There is actually not one sort of year, as generally supposed, but three, depending on the way in which the year is calculated.

The first, which represents one complete turn of 360° around the sun and would certainly be the only year if our planet always described the same orbit, is the sidereal year. This is calculated by taking as reference mark an imaginary line drawn through the sun and a fixed star, that is to say a star having the same movement as the sun in the heart of the galaxy. The time taken between two successive passages of the Earth through this line is 365 days, 6 hours, 9 minutes and 11 seconds.

But this sidereal year is not the one used as the basis of our calendar. What is important to Man is the regular return of the seasons and not the position of the Earth in relation to certain stars. The beginning of each season corresponds to a very specific position of the sun on the horizon (the equator). In summer and winter this position is called the solstice, in spring and autumn, the equinox. The summer solstice is the highest point reached by the sun above the horizon successively in each hemisphere, and from which it then begins to descend. These differences in height modify the lighted areas in the various parts of the terrestrial globe and consequently the lengths of the days and nights. In the northern hemisphere, the longest day is at the summer solstice, the shortest at the winter; the opposite holds good at the same moment in the southern hemisphere. At the equinoxes, day and night are of the same length. Now if spring (the vernal point) is chosen as the starting point of the year, it will be seen that the following year it does not fall at the same point of the orbit but twenty minutes prior to having completed one turn of 360° around the sun. The tropical year, based on the return of the seasons, which is used as the basis of our calendar, is therefore shorter than the sidereal year by about twenty minutes. Its exact duration is 365 days, 5 hours, 48 minutes and 45 seconds.

This discrepancy in the durations of the year according to the choice of reference mark is obviously incompatible with the alleged permanence of the solar system. Newtonians account for it by claiming the rectifying action of solar gravitation on the equatorial bulge, but the most plausible explanation appears to be the following : the solar vortex can be compared to a sphere flattened by its movement of rotation, maximum centrifugal force being exerted at the equator. Now after expulsion by the sun, a planet is not always exactly on the equator of the vortex but passes sometimes below, sometimes above it. This results in the inclination of the axis of rotation and in the various seasons. At the solstice, the pole furtherst removed from the equator of the solar vortex is subjected to less centrifugal force than the pole closer to it. The axis of rotation accordingly adjusts itself slightly. The difference between the tropical and sidereal years is therefore an indication of the evolution to which the axis of the Earth's rotation is subjected.

But there is a third sort of year that merits particular attention. In the course of its circuit, the Earth is not always at the same distance from the sun but periodically passes through a point at which it is the closest (its perihelion) and another at which it is the furthest removed (its aphelion). Now, if the time taken by the Earth to return to the same point—say the aphelion—is calculated, the result is a year of 365 days, 6 hours, 13 minutes and 55 seconds, that is 4 minutes and 45 seconds more than the sidereal year. In other words, the aphelion shifts forward each year in the direction of translation. As this difference cannot be explained by universal gravitation, technical manuals have found it more convenient to elude the problem by calling this year abnormal—

or rather "anomalistic", as this sounds more scientific—and saying nothing more about it.

And yet this is a very important problem, as it affects directly and appreciably the Earth's course around the sun. In view of the fact that nothing occurs in the Universe without reason, this modification in the Earth's path must be explained. Why is the point furthest removed from the sun through which the Earth passes in the course of one circuit not in the same position of the orbit each year? Why does the aphelion shift forward each year in the direction of translation?

Once again a study of evolution supplies the answer. The aphelion shifts forward because the planet describes spirals and not closed orbits. But why does it describe these spirals? Bode's law explained that there is in the heart of the solar system a centrifugal force proportional to the radius, that is, increasing towards the periphery. Now, what happens to a body on which an increasingly strong centrifugal force is being brought to bear? Increase in force produces a deflection on the direction in which motion is taking place equal to the mean between the thrust towards the exterior and the original direction of that motion. This same principle can be observed in a moving automobile. If struck on its side, it is deflected from its course not in a continuation of the direction from which the blow came but in a line which is the resultant of the direction of shock and the direction of its previous motion.

Centrifugal force in the heart of the solar system (so clearly visible in the case of comet tails) is therefore responsible for the yearly shift of the Earth's aphelion in an outward direction. This yearly shift implies the existence of a phenomenon resulting in an increase in orbit: no shift in the aphelion, no enlargement of the orbit; conversely, no enlargement of the orbit, no shift in the aphelion.

If a comparison is now made between two planets, one fictitious and describing a closed circuit, the other real and following its spiral, it will be seen that the first completes one full turn in a period of time corresponding to a sidereal year whereas the second reaches its aphelion 4 minutes and 45 seconds later. This difference in time represents the increase in orbit length due to evolution. At a velocity of 30 km/sec, which is the Earth's speed on its orbit, this increase equals about 8,500 kms. In the case of a not too eccentric orbit, that for convenience sake will be compared to a circle, this increase would correspond to an average increase of 1,350 kms a year in the distance between the Earth and the sun.

As the Earth is halfway between Venus and Mars, which are 120 to 130 million kilometres apart, an average increase in distance of 1,350 kms a year represents a period of 100,000 years in round figures. But the distance between Venus and Mars includes two stages, that is Venus-Earth and Earth-Mars. One stage therefore represents 50,000 years. This indicates that the sun expels a planet every 50,000 years.

The age of the Earth accordingly falls within certain limits. If Mercury was expelled recently, the Earth can only have been in existence for a little more than two 50,000-year stages, that is during the Mercury-Venus and Venus-Earth stages. Its age would consequently be slightly in excess of 100,000 years. If, on the contrary, Mercury is terminating its first stage and approaching the 50,000 mark, then the Earth's age would not be far from 150,000. The figure can accordingly be established between this minimum of 100,000 and maximum of 150,000. At first sight, such a figure must seem low, even unbelievable. This point will be discussed in more detail later on. What must be decided before going any further is whether the real age is closer to the maximum or to the minimum figure.

According to Bode's law, the respective positions of the planets are: Mercury = 4, Venus = 7, the Earth = 10, Mars = 16, etc. These figures are obtained by multiplying each term of a geometric progression by 3 and adding 4 to each product, starting from zero. If the terms of the geometric progression multiplied by 3 are alone taken into consideration, this gives 3 for Venus, 6 for the Earth, 12 for Mars, etc., and if the geometric progression were the only factor involved in the calculation of the position of the planets, Mercury's distance should then equal ½ of 3, that is 1.5. But according to Bode's law, its position corresponds to figure 4. It can therefore be assumed that this figure represents 2.5 for the effect of expulsion and 1.5 for the geometric progression. And as the figure 4 corresponds to approximately 60 million kilometres, the effect of expulsion would be 38 million kilometres and that of the progressive increase in distance 22 million.

It is important, however, not to be led astray. The effect of expulsion does not cease from the moment that the planet loses contact with the sun. Neither does the former immediately start to describe well-defined orbits solely under the influence of centrifugal force proportional to the radius. The initial impulse persists for a very long time. If a study is made not of the positions of the planets but of the distance (expressed in millions of kilometres) that they move away from the sun over a period of 50,000 years, the following will be noted :

Mercury, passing from 59 to 104, moves away 45 ;

Venus, passing from 104 to 148 (the Earth), moves away 44 (1) ;

The Earth, passing from 148 to 237 (Mars), moves away 89 (2) ;

Mars, passing from 237 to 414 (the Asteroids), moves away 177 (4) ;

The Asteroids, passing from 414 to 770 (Jupiter), move away 356 (8) ;

Jupiter, passing from 770 to 1,480 (Saturn), moves away 710 (16) ;

Saturn, passing from 1,480 to 2,900 (Uranus), moves away 1,420 (32).

It will be clear from this table that it is only from the position of Venus onwards, that is, from a distance of about 100 million kilometres from the sun, that the moving away follows a geometric progression. The initial impulse therefore is still felt not only from the sun to Mercury but even from Mercury to Venus, which has moved away 45 million kilometres instead of 22 (half the 44 million increase in distance of the planet next in line : the Earth).

It can therefore be assumed that the initial impulse, which diminishes through the ages, plays a very important role in the annual moving away of the planet after its expulsion. The theoretic 22 million kilometres representing this progressive moving away therefore correspond not to a complete period of 50,000 years but to a fraction, probably less than the half. The age of Mercury is accordingly calculated as being 20,000 years, which brings that of Venus to 70,000 and of the Earth to 120,000.

It should be emphasized that the 120,000 years mentioned above do not correspond to 120,000 revolutions of the Earth around the sun because, close to the sun, the planetary orbits lasted appreciably less time. Mercury's year corresponds to 88 days and Venus' to 225. During the 50,000 years which mark the intermediate period between the Venus point (a year of 225 days) and that of the Earth (a year of 365 days), our planet revolved approximately 58,000 times around the sun ; between the Mercury and Venus positions, 145,000 times ; and during the 20,000 years prior to Mercury's present position, approximately 100,000 times. Accordingly, the number of orbits that the Earth has made around the sun during these 120,000 years must amount to at least 300,000. It is even probable that the exact number is appreciably higher if, immediately after its expulsion, the planet turned around the sun faster than the sun on its own axis, as is the case at present with Phobos, a recent satellite of Mars, which revolves around Mars three times during one rotation of the planet on its own axis. If, at the beginning, Mercury described one orbit around the sun in less than 25 days as compared with the 88 days it now takes, its present position could represent 10,000 to 20,000 years more than has just been calculated. Its age would, in that case, be as much as 40,000 years, that of Venus 90,000 and that of the Earth 140,000.

Consequently, our planet, which would have made approximately 200,000 turns during these additional 20,000 years, would have made a total of 500,000 orbits around the sun up to the present day. However, as this is nothing but an assumption which can only be verified when conditions of expulsion are better known or when the number of varva corresponding to the Earth's orbits have been more accurately established in the terrains, the figure of 120,000 years, corresponding to 300,000 orbits, can be provisionally accepted.

These figures are obviously very rough. The exact result depends in fact on the distance to which the planet was expelled, a distance that would seem to be not less than 38 million kilometres, but could be greater. However, the differences can only range between a minimum of 100,000 years and a maximum of 150,000. The essential is not to try, right away, to supply precise figures which may later prove to be erroneous but to indicate the path to be followed if exact results are to be obtained. The discrepancies regarding the Earth's age are such that, before going on to more specific figures, the question of magnitude must be clarified in order to decide if this age amounts to hundreds of thousands, millions or milliards of years.

As the figures that have just been arrived at are more than 10,000 times smaller than those accepted by the majority of physicists, whose calculations are based on radioactive phenomena, it would now be advisable to undertake a close examination of these results on the basis of a certain number of comparisons.

III : Astronomical comparisons

(1) *Hubble's law excludes the milliard figure as scale of the Earth's age.*

As has already been seen in the general considerations of Subsection I, above, distances between the centres of the galaxies increase in a proportion of approximately ½ milliardth a year.

Consequently, if calculations are made back through the ages on the basis of this same proportion, the Universe would have had a zero radius 2 milliard years ago. As the sun is a product of the galaxy, its age must be appreciably less than these 2 milliard years. As to the age of the Earth—expelled by the sun after Mars, the Asteroids, Jupiter, Saturn, Uranus, Neptune, Pluto and all the other planets expelled even earlier and now disintegrated—this age can only be a tiny fraction of that of the sun. Hubble's law on the expansion of the Universe therefore excludes the milliard figure as a measure of the Earth's age.

(2) *Hubble's law confirms the results based on the advance of the Earth's aphelion (or on the differences between the durations of the anomalistic and sidereal years).*

As the solar system is part of the galaxy, its expansion, which results in the progressive moving away of the planets, must be in the same proportion as galactic expansion, which results in the speeding away of the nebulae. There is nevertheless one peculiarity to be taken into account. The solar system occupies a fairly eccentric position in the heart of the galaxy and its expansion must therefore be slightly greater than the average for the galaxy as a whole. As is known, in all vortexes, expansion is not the same from the centre to the periphery but increases in proportion to distance from the centre, as demonstrated by Bode's law.

The galaxy closest to ours is 3 million light years away. In a Universe which is a plenum, galaxies touch. Consequently, this distance of 3 million light years, which represents two half-diameters (that of our galaxy and of the nearest) can be considered the average diameter of a galaxy. According to Hubble's law, expansion occurs at the rate of 160 million km/sec per million light-years, that is, approximately 15 milliard kilometres per year : a proportion of ½ milliardth of the diameter of the galaxy.

The star closest to the sun is 4 light years away. This figure can accordingly be adopted as the diameter of the solar system. In the peripheral zone beyond Uranus, the planets are moving away more or less uniformly at the rate of 1,500 million kilometres per 50,000 years (see Subsection II, above). This represents 30,000 kilometres a year or an annual increase of 60,000 kilometres in the diameter of the solar system. As this diameter is 4 light years, annual expansion is in a proportion of 1½ milliardths.

In other words, the rate of expansion of the solar system (a proportion of 1½ milliardths a year) is the same as that of the galaxy (a proportion of ½ milliardth). The 3 : 1 ratio is explained by the eccentric position of the sun, the vortex expansion of which is necessarily greater than the average for the galaxy as a whole. In any case, it is reasonable to assume that the "life" of the sun is shorter than that of the galaxy. The contrary would be untenable.

The comparison can be made in another way. The solar system has a diameter of 4 light years. Consequently 750,000 similar systems could be juxtaposed on a galactic diameter. But as the galactic diameter increases by 15 milliard kilometres a year, mean expansion is at the rate of 20,000 kilometres a year for each stellar system. Ours, increasing by 60,000 kilometres instead of 20,000 therefore has an expansion three times greater than the average. As has been seen, this is quite explicable.

It is altogether illogical to assume that galactic expansion occurs without the participation of the stellar systems which form its constituent parts. In fact the expansion of a galaxy is clearly nothing but the sum of the expansion of its various parts. The solar system therefore cannot be a permanent system in the heart of an expanding galaxy but expands too—in conformity with both the general galactic development and its individual position in the heart of the system as a whole.

As the position of the solar system is an eccentric one in the galaxy, its expansion in the proportion of 1½ milliardths a year is therefore in keeping with the mean galactic expansion in the proportion of ½ milliardth. Hubble's law on the speeding away of the galaxies and Bode's law on the positions of the planets consequently agree very satisfactorily. In short, Hubble's law confirms the correctness of the figures obtained on the basis of the advance of the aphelion, that is, an annual increase of 1,350 kilometres in the Earth's distance from the sun.

IV : Geological comparisons

No method designed to calculate the age of the Earth can be valid if the results are not in accord with the evidence contained in its terrains. It will now be necessary to compare the figures just arrived at with geological facts.

Geologists are divided with regard to the age of the Earth, some supporting the short-scale theory, others the long. The latter are obviously influenced by the assertions of the specialists in radioactivity. Certain geological findings do, as a matter of fact, appear to indicate that the Earth is of a very great age. For example, the crystallization of rock cannot be explained by present conditions on the Earth. Some writers think that the phenomenon can be more easily interpreted if the periods in question are considerably increased. But this procedure is only admissible if the relevant process is a very slow one ; on the other hand, if nothing happens in certain given conditions, it is not by increasing the time factor that something will be encouraged to occur. Another reason that leads geologists to accept long chronology is the fact that certain mountain chains do not belong to the same period in the east and in the west. They have inferred from this that the chain took millions of years to be formed. Now this peculiarity, as has already been seen, is explained by the slow rotation of the Earth which created widely varied conditions on the surface of the globe depending on longitude, with the result that in one hemisphere various zones simultaneously traversed geological periods that are generally assumed to be successive (Chapter Six, Section 3). Plication consequently appears to have taken place over thousands of years whereas it is, in fact, the result of a very abrupt movement occurring almost simultaneously from one end of the chain to the other.

The supporters of the short scale base their assumptions on various phenomena which necessarily limit the age of the Earth. Chief among these is the process of erosion which wears away the continents and, each year, carries enormous quantities of material into the seas. For example, E. de Martonne estimates at 570 m³ per km² the annual erosion of the north face of the Alps. If millions of years had passed since their formation in the Tertiary era, they should by now have completely disappeared whereas, in fact, several of their peaks exceed 4,000 metres. It is therefore impossible to calculate by millions of years the time lapse between the Tertiary era and the present day. As for the idea that there was less erosion in the past than now, this is quite illogical. A new high chain of mountains recently formed and not yet consolidated is subject to much greater erosion than old rock hardened by time.

The Alps are not an exception. In Katanga, for example, erosion is even greater and, according to M. Robert, attains 500 to 700 m³ per km². On the basis of an annual average of 10 km³ for the erosion of the entire Earth, A. de Lapparent has reckoned that it should lead to the complete disappearance of the continents in seven million years. Clearly this is a long way from the milliards of years suggested by the specialists in radioactivity.

As the continents exist and are a long way from disappearing, and as terrains perfectly identifiable with previous periods can be found, it is absolutely impossible that these can have existed for several million years. Their real age cannot be more than a fraction of a million.

The most enthusiastic supporters of short chronology are those geologists who have been struck by the seasonal alternations visible in the terrain. Sediments formed during periods of considerable light are lighter than those accumulated during periods of darkness or of shadow. As already mentioned, the Swedish geologist, de Geer, when studying the withdrawal of the last glacier of the Quaternary era in Scandinavia, noticed that when the sea flooded the land, it deposited clay bands in small alternating light and dark beds, the light ones corresponding to summer sedimentation and the dark ones to winter. One light bed and one dark constituted what he termed a varva, that is, sedimentation over one year. Studying the withdrawal of the ice and counting carefully the number of varvas, de Geer and his students managed to identify 14,000 from the end of the glacial period to the present day.

This result requires explanation. The varvas which were formed between the Deluge (3,500 B. C.) and the present day, that is, over a period of approximately 5,500 years, correspond to years like those of the present day, but this is not so in the case of those covering the transition period between the last glaciation and the Deluge, at which time the Earth was turning on its axis at the rate of one rotation every two months. The alternation in the light and dark beds at that time consequently correspond to this special rotation. These 8,500 varvas therefore only amount to about 1,500 years, making a total of around 7,000 years between the last glaciation and the present day.

It is, accordingly, a very short period that bridges the gap between prehistoric and historic times and the hiatus created by the theory of long chronology now disappears. There is no longer a sudden and inexplicable jump between the hundreds of thousands of years during which Man was supposed to have lived in caves and pile dwellings and the fourth millenium B. C., with its small human communities. Humanity developed very quickly as soon as climatic conditions were favourable. The assertion that prehistoric man lived for hundreds of thousands and even millions of years is categorically refuted by the small number of stone tools that have been discovered.   Although nothing like their totality has yet been unearthed, their number is nevertheless so small that it can only correspond to a very reduced population.   As it is not possible to assume that there was at that period only one man per cave every two or three centuries, the inevitable conclusion is that the prehistoric period of Man was very short, as confirmed by the studies of the Swedish geologists.

Previous geological periods should therefore be studied with the certainty that not more than about 7,000 years elapsed between the end of the glaciations and the present day.   It is a pity that de Geer's method has not been widely adopted, as seasonal alternations have been discovered in many terrains.   J. E. Pompeckj has noted them in the Souabe stage of the Lower Jurassic period; J. E. Marr in the Silurian in England; H. Korn in the Thuringian stage of the Lower Carboniferous; G. Richter-Bernbourg in the German Zechstein stage.   As the findings of these workers considerably reduced the chronologies generally accepted, they tried to "rig" them, in order to make them coincide, by putting forward the theory that these alternations corresponded to variations in solar activity—cycles of 11 years according to Korn and of 35 years according to Pompeckj.   But in spite of these theories, they did not manage to reconcile the differences, so great were they.   There is obviously no excuse for modifying accurate results in order to make them tally with the erroneous figures of physicists.

The geological method of determining the age of the Earth by seasonal strata is certainly the best and the most reliable.   As has been seen, the areas which were at the dawn and twilight positions passed, as a consequence of slow rotation, through alternations of light and darkness which left traces in the terrains.   It is therefore possible to count the number of times that the Earth turned around the sun during this period.   Similar alternations occurred in the regions of the polar circles and cross checking can therefore be carried out.   In fact, in one and the same hemisphere, alternations occur simultaneously in the east (twilight point), at the pole (midday position) and in the west (dawn position) and correspond in each of these three areas to three different geological periods. Comparisons of these alternations should make it possible to establish the duration of these geological periods, the speed of rotation in relation to translation, and the position of the continents. The importance of their systematic study cannot be too strongly emphasized.

Until such a study is undertaken, there is no alternative but to rely on incomplete facts. Coal beds constitute a case in point and will now be examined.

The majority of coal deposits conform to a certain pattern. The coal forms more or less thick beds in detrital sediment the lower layer of which is called the wall and the upper layer the roof. Roots are frequently found in the wall, upright trunks in the roof. Now, surprisingly, in the formation of these deposits, the seams, including their walls and roofs, are superimposed a considerable number of times: in the Franco-Belgian basin for example more than 400 times, and in the Sarre-Lorraine basin, 88. There is unquestionably a periodicity in this phenomenon.

Now it is impossible to explain this periodicity on the basis of long chronology. According to the specialists in radioactivity, the Carboniferous period lasted 85 million years. In the case of the Westphalian production, the sedimentary thickness of which represents approximately 1/20th of this period, this would accordingly correspond to something a little in excess of 4 million years. The 400 layers of this basin would therefore each have taken 10,000 years to be formed. But there is nothing that can explain these particular conditions occurring every ten thousand years. The theory of variations in solar activity has again been put forward. However, coal formation was an essentially local phenomenon that occurred in the lagoons, and if this theory were correct there would necessarily be other evidence of such exceptional and inexplicable solar activity. Furthermore, all experts agree that these coal beds must have been covered very rapidly otherwise the plant layer would have been destroyed and not carbonized. Another proof of the rapidity of the process is supplied by the swellings that formed on the upright trunks during consolidation of the mass. Obviously if the plant layer had taken thousands of years to be consolidated before being covered, there would be no such swellings as the elements—wind, rain, etc.—would have carried everything away. These various factors—unusual flora of the Carboniferous period, rapidity of formation of walls, of destruction of forests and of subsequent covering over by the roof—have already been examined [1] and will not be dealt with again here.

To summarize, the periodicity of the phenomenon and its localization in the lagoons can only be satisfactorily explained in the following way : when the Earth turned slowly on its own axis, the areas in the dawn and twilight positions (those at the midday point in the polar regions as well) passed alternately, as a result of the inclination of the terrestrial axis, from light to darkness in the course of one translation of the planet around the sun. During the darkness period, which lasted for months at a time, snow and and ice were formed and then melted as soon as they moved into the light. The thaw carried with it into the lagoons abundant material that formed what is called the "wall". Between the water and the uninterrupted heat (there was no nocturnal cooling off again for several months), an outburst of vegetation took place. The lagoon very quickly became covered by a thickly entangled forest. Trees grew with extraordinary rapidity. Their fossilized trunks give no evidence of any slowing down of growth due to winter conditions. Everything was formed in one season during prolonged sunlight, then everything was destroyed, again very rapidly, and the rains which occurred when the area passed once more through the intermediate zone between light and darkness covered the coal bed with its "roof". The marine rise caused by

[1] *La Terre s'en va*, by Louis JACOT, p. 154 et seq., Editions de la Table Ronde, Paris.

the melting of the ice in the areas that were moving more and more into the sun frequently flooded the lagoons. Marine fauna is often found in the roof, but never in the coal. This is a clear indication of seasonal fluctuation. Thereafter, the lagoon passed into darkness and snow and ice reformed, preventing all plant growth. Roots are consequently never found in the roof. Then the cycle started all over again.

One coal bed was accordingly laid in the course of one year and not of 10,000, as asserted by the supporters of long chronology. The Westphalian basin was therefore formed during 400 translations of the Earth around the sun and not in 4 million years. The age accepted by the supporters of the long scale must now be divided by 10,000 in order to obtain the exact age of the Earth. From 1.5 milliard years this then drops to 150,000 and agrees with the figure supplied by astronomical data.

V : Comparisons in the field of physics

In the Earth describes spirals around the sun and each year completes one orbital revolution longer than the preceding one, this must necessarily take more time. Now, by assuming the same number of seconds for all revolutions, man increases his time standard each year. Admittedly, this increase, which is minimal, does not affect current measurements, but when certain phenomena are studied—for example, the velocity of light, the kilometre-per-second rate of which is very high (nearly 300,000)—it inevitably becomes noticeable.

It is not sufficient merely to measure the velocity of light twice at an interval of one year and calculate the difference in order to obtain the change in the length of a second. In a Universe in which everything is in the process of evolving, not only does the time standard evolve but light phenomenon as well. But the evolution of these two factors is not identical and calls for closer study.

In the heart of the solar vortex, evolution manifests itself in the form of expansion of all the constituent particles of the medium in which the celestial bodies are being carried along. This general expansion towards the exterior of the vortex produces the centrifugal force that each year causes the planets to move further away from the sun. Now this expansion is not the same throughout the vortex. Bode's law has shown, on the contrary, by its factor-2 geometric progression that it increases in proportion to distance from the sun. The annual distance that the Earth moves away from the sun is therefore the result not only of the expansion of the ether particles close to it but also of all those which separate it from the sun. It is therefore proportional to the mean expansion of the particles situated between Mercury (from which the factor-2 geometric progression begins) and our planet. This mean expansion is found at Venus' distance where, according to Bode's law, the mean increase of the particles is only half the mean increase at the Earth's distance.

On the other hand, a calculation of the velocity of light on or near the Earth is based on the expansion of particles whose increase is total, that is, twice the average increase. The evolution that occurs from one year to another therefore has twice as much effect on the velocity of light as on the length of a second.

The increase in the diameter of the particles transmitting light is shown by a decrease in the velocity of the light. Consequently two phenomena with opposite effects are found here: on the one hand, the decrease in the velocity of light should result in an increase in the number of seconds, but on the other, the lengthening of the time standard should result in a decrease in the number of seconds (the standard being longer). If these two phenomena were equal, their effects would cancel each other out and there would be no difference between two successive years. But as the evolutionary process has twice as much effect on the velocity of light as on the lengthening of the second, far from cancelling each other out they lead to what at first sight seems paradoxical : the actual decrease in the velocity of light produces a fictitious shortening of the length of a second more or less equal to its actual lengthening. This can be compared to a taxi with two metres, one recording only half the number of kilometres covered (and designed for the client), the other recording the exact number (and designed for the owner). The chauffeur, having been paid 100 francs, would be in the position of having to pay 200 to his employer. For the chauffeur, the 100-franc sum recorded on the meter would represent not what he had really earned but what he had actually lost. This question has been dealt with in greater detail elsewhere and will not be further enlarged upon here.

If, now, the tests that Michelson carried out over a period of 47 years on the velocity of light are examined, it will be seen that the results of each test were always less than those of the preceding one and that the velocity of light which, in 1879, was 299,910 km/sec dropped to 299,769 in 1926. The difference of 114 kilometres in 47 years represents 2 kms 425 metres a year.

This apparent reduction of 2 kms 425 metres in 299,910 denotes that the duration of the second in fact increased in the same proportion (approximately one eight millionth) and that the sidereal year, which contained 31,558,149 seconds in the previous revolution, should have had 255 seconds less in the following revolution (as the time standard had lengthened). At the rate of 30 km/sec (average velocity of the Earth on its orbit), the extra 255 seconds accorded each successive sidereal year represent a lengthening of the orbit of 7,650 kms or an annual mean increase of about 1,200 kms in the distance of the Earth from the sun. The distance between Mars and Venus being approximately 120 million kilometres, it would therefore take 100,000 years for this to be covered, or 50,000 years for the Earth's orbit to equal that of Mars.

In short, calculations based on a decrease in the velocity of light lead to results that are very close to those obtained by the astronomic method based on the shift in the aphelion. They are also perfectly in keeping with the results arrived at by geological

Universal Evolution

TABLE OF HISTORY OF THE EARTH

Origin: Earth expelled by the sun.

First phase: Translation of the Earth around the sun, without rotation.

Archean age: The Earth, like Mars at the present time, revolved around the sun showing always the same face.

Second phase: Very slow rotation of the Earth.

	Dawn	Midday	Twilight	Night
Primary Era (including Algonkian)				
1st Rtn. ...	Lower Algonkian	Mid-Algonkian	Upper Algonkian	Upper Algonkian Lower Cambrian
2nd Rtn. ...	Lower and mid-Cambrian	Upper Cambrian Lower Silurian	Mid- and Upper Silurian	Upper Silurian Lower Devonian
3rd Rtn. ...	Lower Devonian	Mid-Devonian	Upper Devonian Lower Carboniferous	Mid-Carboniferous
4th Rtn. ...	Upper Carboniferous Lower Permian	Mid-Permian	Upper Permian	Upper Permian Lower Triassic
Secondary Era				
5th Rtn. ...	Mid- and Upper Triassic Lower Jurassic	Mid- and Upper Jurassic	Upper Jurassic Lower and Mid-Cretaceous	Upper Cretaceous Expulsion of moon Lower Eocene Dislocation of continents

Tertiary Era

6th Rtn. ...	Lower and Mid-Eocene	Upper Eocene Oligocene	Oligocene Miocene	Miocene-Pliocene Günz glaciation

Quaternary Era (Man's appearance on the Earth and inter-glacial period)

	Stage	Man	Culture	Glaciation
7th Rtn. ...	Sicilian	Pithecanthropus Sinanthropus	Pre-Chellean	Mindel
8th Rtn. ...	Tyrrhenian	Heidelberg and Swanscombe	Chellean Acheulean	Riss
9th Rtn. ...	Flandrian	Neanderthal	Acheulean Mousterian	Würm

Third phase : Accelerated rotation of the Earth

Transition Period	Upper Paleolithic	Grimaldi Cro-Magnon	Aurignacian Solutrean	Melting and partial re-forming of glaciers
	Mesolithic	Chancelade	Magdalenian	
	Neolithic	Homo sapiens	Huts Domestication of animals Cultivation of grain Metals Pottery	

Fourth phase : Daily rotation of the Earth

Historic Period	The Deluge (3.500 B. C.) *Early civilizations* *Historic times*			Sudden melting of glaciers Stabilization of climates

methods, particularly in connection with the study of the formation of coal deposits. This similarity in results obtained by methods belonging to spheres as varied as those of physics, astronomy and geology is striking—surely a clear sign that the evolutionary process makes itself felt from one end of the Universe to the other and affects all scientific fields.

The spectacular nature of evolution stands out for all to see.

12. Table of history of the Earth

On the basis of the review that has now been made of the Earth's past and of the principle events that marked its existence —glaciations, marine rises and falls, plications, expulsion of the moon, dislocation of the continents, etc.—a table has been drawn up to show how the various periods resulting from slow rotation gradually developed. This table, which will be found on pages 138 and 139, has been based essentially on information regarding climates and sea level variations contained in Maurice Gignoux's remarkably well-documented book "Géologie stratigraphique" and on the data found in Moret's excellent works, "Paléontologie animale" and "Paléontologie végétale". The connections established between the dawn, midday, twilight and night positions of the globe and the various geological strata were taken from one of the author's previous works [1].

13. The Earth's future or the unpleasant truth

Having reviewed the main events that formerly caused great upheavals in the life of our planet, it is natural to wonder whether such trials are likely to recur.

---

[1] *La Terre s'en va*, by Louis JACOT, Editions de la Table Ronde, Paris.

The evolution that governs the fate of the Earth does not consist of an automatic repetition of events that are always similar. On the contrary, it has been seen that in the past it affected terrestrial rotation in a very specific way by a motion that was slow at first and then gathered speed through the ages. The effects of this slow rotation, such as the immense glaciations that were formed in the hemisphere plunged in continuous darkness and the marine rises resulting from the subsequent melting of the ice, are of course no longer to be feared, but the irrevocable advance of evolution will have other effects that are not all pleasant to envisage.

The progressive increase in distance between the Earth and the sun cannot fail to reduce, little by little, the amount of heat received. The results of certain tests carried out to calculate the temperature on Mars are not very encouraging.

With increasing distance, the surrounding medium will exert less pressure on the terrestrial globe, all the physical particles of which will participate in general expansion. Physical bodies will become more and more unstable. Radioactivity, which at present only affects certain elements (the heaviest), will gradually descend the scale of bodies, extending by degrees from the more complex to the simplest. The terrestrial globe will slowly pass from the solid to the gaseous state.

The more a planet increases in size, the more does the velocity of the ambient medium vary on its diurnal and nocturnal faces (Kepler's law : see Chapter Five, Section 2). Inevitably the planet turns faster and faster. The example has already been given of Jupiter which is 1,300 times more voluminous than the Earth and yet turns on its axis in less than 10 hours whereas our globe takes 24. The decrease in density as a consequence of expansion and of the decrease in the surrounding pressure is such that Jupiter no longer rotates as one block, its velocity being 9 hours and 50 minutes at the equator and 9 hours and 55 minutes near the poles.

Also, the more the velocity of rotation increases and the pressure of the ambient medium decreases, the more the planet becomes deformed and the more frequently does it expel satellites.

The expulsion of planets by the sun and of satellites by the planets is, as has been seen (Chapter Five, Section 3), a periodic process. In the solar mass, it occurs approximately every 50,000 years. As to the interval of time between the expulsion of satellites by the planets, this has not yet been determined. It is certainly shorter. Mars, the diameter of which is appreciably smaller than that of the Earth but which is 50,000 years older, already has a second satellite. It can therefore be assumed that our planet will expel a second moon before reaching the position at which Mars is situated at the moment. The Asteroids (the result of the debris of a disintegrated planet) obviously cannot be taken as an example, but Jupiter, still further removed and 150,000 years older than the Earth has numerous satellites that appear to be the result of nine successive expulsions. If it is assumed that the phenomenon started at a point halfway between Venus and the Earth, then 20,000 years would appear to be the average time lapse between expulsions. Admittedly, calculations cannot be made on the basis of an average because expulsions, as a consequence of acceleration of rotation and decrease in cohesion, appear to occur at increasingly closer intervals. However, these figures of 50,000 and 20,000 years can be accepted as the maximum or minimum period that can elapse between the expulsion of the moon and that of the next satellite. The exact figure is probably closer to the minimum than the maximum; the example of Mars, due to its reduced volume, is not very conclusive.

The terrestrial globe is already very deformed. Its diameter at the equator measures 43 kilometres more than the distance between the two poles. This represents something of a hump! Also it should not be supposed that the event will not occur merely because it is undesirable. Evolution does not take such considerations into account.

As the expulsion of our first satellite occurred in the Tertiary era, that is, probably more than 20,000 years ago, the next similar occurrence is perhaps closer than is generally imagined. It would suffice that terrestrial rotation, in keeping with the general process of evolution, picked up speed for these events to be hastened.

Is it possible at the present time to establish which will be the part of the globe to be expelled? One thing is certain and that is that it will not be in the area of the poles. As to the regions on the equator, the one in which it is the most likely to occur is the one furthest removed from the axis of rotation. Now, as the density of water is three times less than that of rock, the ocean zones are, for reasons of balance, further removed from the axis of rotation than the continental blocks, paradoxical as this may seem. So, as it is the eccentric area that moves continuously away through progressive deformation, it would seem at first sight that the largest marine mass, the Pacific, will be expelled. But the heaviest elements are normally ejected in such circumstances, so the continent closest to the large marine deeps, that is, the American continent situated between the Atlantic and the Pacific, appears to be the most closely threatened. The total volume of water on the Earth's surface (1,300 million km^3) would in any case not be nearly sufficient to form a second satellite which will probably not be so very different from the first, the moon, the volume of which is 20 milliard km^3.

This theory, based solely on the probable moving away of an area in relation to the axis of rotation, should obviously be studied anew when the globe's deformations are better known.

The seas will play an important part in the upheavals that will occur at the time of the next expulsion as they cover 7/10ths of the globe (360 million km^2) whereas the land areas only occupy 3/10ths (150 million km^2). Their volume is therefore thirteen times greater than that of the emerged land (1,300 million km^3 as opposed to 100 million) and extensive immersions should be expected.

The expulsion of a continent will probably modify the sea-land balance of the surface of the globe, so it would be logical to suppose that upheavals similar to those that occurred after the expulsion of the moon—dislocation and drift of the continents, plications, volcanic eruptions, etc.—will occur.

These will be grave trials for humanity to face. The survival of Man raises problems that he would be wise to reflect on in advance in order that precautions may be taken in good time.

CHAPTER VII

EVOLUTION OF MATTER

1. What is matter?

This study would not be complete if, having examined the effect of evolution on the galaxies, the celestial bodies and our Earth, it were not pursued into the field of the infinitesimally small. It goes without saying that in a Universe in which all phenomena are related, those at the macrocosmic level being but the consequence of those at the microcosmic, it is only by a study of the behaviour of elementary particles that the phenomena occurring at larger scales will be understood.

This study has already been anticipated to quite an extent in Chapters Three and Four, where the unity of matter and the structure of the Universe were considered. As this question has also been covered elsewhere [1] only the essential points will be summarized here.

It might be as well to start with a brief review of the facts noted by physicists and the conclusions they have drawn from them. The simplest elements concerned in chemical reactions are called atoms. They were considered to be indivisible. Ninety-three such elements have been classified, according to their "atomic" weight and their chemical properties. They range from helium, the lightest, to uranium, the heaviest. Investiga-

---

[1] *L'Univers en marche*, Nouvelles Editions Latine, Paris, *Eléments de physique évolutive*, Editions du Scorpion, Paris, *Méditations sur le Mouvement*, Editions du Scorpion, Paris, all by Louis JACOT.

tions into radioactivity subsequently revealed that certain of these elements, till then considered undividable, actually do divide, either naturally or as a result of bombardment by certain particles (induced radioactivity). This discovery, however, gave no information as to the structure of the atom. It was then that Rutherford, studying the passage of alpha particles through a thin sheet of metal, was struck by the rarity of the large deviations. He concluded that the greater part of the atom was empty and that almost its entire mass was concentrated in a minute part, the nucleus, with a positive charge which repelled the particles, thus producing the large deviations observed from time to time, whereas the negative electrons, held by the force of "gravitation" of the nucleus, circled about at relatively large distances. In this context, the atom consequently represented a tiny planetary system. This theory was taken up and developed by Bohr.

The "planetary" conception of the atom, however, is not acceptable, for the following reasons :

(1) It does not go to the root of the problem ; it starts at the level of aggregated particles instead of going right down to the elementary particle itself. It consequently presents matter in separate parts that appear to be completely unrelated. Electrons, protons, neutrons, etc., are considered as having different natures.

(2) It does not take into account the fact that motion constitutes the very essence of the particles comprising the atom. By submitting *a priori* that their essential properties are inertia and so-called universal gravitation, it regards motion as a quality foreign to matter. Now it goes without saying that gravitation is incapable of producing explosions—which are daily occurrences—and that any form of matter whose essence is inertia and not motion cannot be dynamic by nature as is the physical world that answers to Einstein's

famous formula: $e = mc^2$ that establishes mass-energy equivalence.

(3) It is contradictory to the extent that it is based on the principle that the mass is endowed with general force of gravitation and at the same time admits that the protons (which are assumed to constitute the greater part of the mass) thrust each other away and only attract the electrons.

(4) It creates, by remaining at the scale of the aggregate instead of going down to the elementary particle, an unbridgeable gap between the material and immaterial worlds and thereby makes the Universe completely incomprehensible.

In order to reply adequately to the question: What is matter? one must constantly keep in mind the fundamental truth that the Universe does not contain substances of different natures, the intrinsic nature of all substance being motion. There cannot be and there are no "motions" that have different "natures".

Once the unity of universal matter and its dynamic nature have been recognized, it has to be admitted that this substance is composed of particles that limit each other mutually because one force can only be observed through its effect on another force, and this implies the existence of limits. (As is known, pressure is equal to the exertion of force on a given surface.)

As the essence of the elementary particles is motion, they spread out until such time as they encounter a resistance equal to the pressure they exert. Always in contact one with the other —this automatically excludes the possibility of a vacuum in the Universe—they constantly compensate each other's movements, the strongest transmitting its surplus to the one that has less. This continuous process of cancelling out of motions finally results in all the particles having the same amount of motion (see Plate 7).

This does not mean that they are all of the same size and therefore of the same density. On the contrary, as has already been seen, universal matter forms enormous vortexes in the centres of which concentric pressure is considerably greater than at the periphery. Consequently it is normal that the particles there—dynamic by nature and therefore pliable—are much more compressed than those in the peripheral zones. Because of this compression, the particles prevent the light rays from passing; this not only causes them to become opaque but makes them appear to be different from those that undulate. There is, however, no basis for assuming that the compressed particles are different from the others, as their density is purely the result of their dynamic nature.

It is customary to consider that ether, being immaterial, is of a totally different nature from matter. In fact, the difference is merely a question of density, matter being nothing but condensed ether.

Having detected the electron (negative), the proton (positive) and the neutron (neutral), physicists discovered a constantly increasing number of particles differing in their mass, load, spin and isospin. They called them positrons, antiprotons, hyperons (lamda, sigma, ksi particles, heavier than the neutron), mesons (intermediary mass between electron and proton, forming several families such as muon, pion, kaon), antineutrons (endowed with wave functions other than the neutron), neutrinos (endowed with extraordinary penetrating power), etc. There are at the present time 34 types of particles and as many antiparticles. As five or six more are discovered every year, the tribe is constantly increasing. A very large number of them do not exist for more than a millionth of a second. In short, the work of physicists, instead of contributing to the unity of matter, has led to an extreme diversity. This is unquestionably an indication that the studies carried out by physicists are not at the level of the elementary particle.

If the characteristics of these particles are closely examined, it will be seen that they differ not in their nature but their motion, particularly their rotation. This can be either clockwise or counterclockwise and constitutes the difference between positive and negative. Mass is nothing but quantity of motion; it is a quantitative, not a qualitative factor and does not imply a difference of nature. As to the extremely short duration of the greater part of the particles, this indicates precisely that they are not elementary but, being only fractions of the whole, are absorbed by the units which surround them, immediately after their emission (Chapter Two, Section 7; Chapter Three, Section 1. See also earlier work by the author [1]). It goes without saying that these particles do not drop into the void but merely disappear as units because they do not have the dynamic scope of an elementary particle.

2. Formation and structure of atoms

The best method of understanding the formation and structure of atoms is to follow mentally the evolutionary process in universal substance, not in its present phase of expansion and general disintegration but in the phase that preceded it, that of the concentration and formation of bodies. (It will not be forgotten (Chapter Three, Sections 3 and 4) that the Universe goes through successive contraction and expansion phases.)

When universal substance, having reached the end of its expansion process, the effect of which is the disintegration of all bodies, passes to the contraction stage, the particles in the central areas of the forming vortexes are subject to considerable pressures that cause them to unite in the form of atoms. They do not, however, unite in just *any* fashion. Particles are spherical and actuated by internal movement. In contact at their equators, they couple when, like two saw-toothed wheels in gear, they turn in opposite directions. If, on the other hand, they turn in the same direction, they superimpose themselves on their poles and

[1] *Méditations sur le mouvement*, Chap. III, by Louis JACOT, Editions du Scorpion, Paris.

thereby form axles. All atoms are in fact gear wheels in motion, made up of couples and axles. Their positions can be established by visualizing the formation process : two couples bound together form a group of four particles. By mentally superimposing two such groups correctly, a set of eight particles will be formed of which only the two negative elements are superimposed ; they are bound to four positive elements (protons), in their turn bound to two negative peripheral elements (electrons). This group is nothing other than the helium atom. The alternation in positive and negative element is accounted for by the fact that the particles in contact move in opposite directions.

The atoms of all bodies are, in fact, sets of helium atoms, as demonstrated by radioactivity, the emitted alpha and beta particles being the debris of such atoms. The manner in which these sets are constituted can be imagined by carrying out their reconstruction theoretically. The principal rules to be observed are those of dynamic balance. Atoms should be neither indefinitely superimposed through their axles nor excessively juxtaposed at their equators as in such circumstances they would obviously be unstable and would not satisfy the conditions of concentric pressure which are the basis of their formation.

Furthermore, particles of the same symbol repel one another (as do two wheels moving in the same direction) when they establish contact at their equators, whereas particles of opposite symbol interlock, their opposing movements causing them to actuate each other mutually. These sets would accordingly consist of alternating particles—positive, negative, positive, negative, etc.—in contact, the superimposed particles all turning in the same direction.

If, on the basis of this procedure, several helium atoms are put together, it will be seen that their juxtaposed axles form successive shells (A.B.C.D.E.F.G.) starting from axle A (the central axle of the atom). Accordingly, the peripheral electrons of these atoms will also be situated in different shells. But physicists have recognized precisely that these electrons are distributed in various shells to which they have assigned the letters K.L.M.N.O.P.Q. It is obvious that the electrons in shell K are the ones bound to the axle in A, those in L to B, etc. As the structure of the various nuclei (neon, argon, krypton, etc.) has already been described [1] and shows that only such a formation of the nucleus can explain the position of the peripheral electrons, this diagrammatic way of illustrating the atom will not be gone into in more detail here.

A little thought regarding atomic structure will make it clear that the particles moving in the centre of the atom are much more compressed than those at the periphery. (As is known, concentric pressure in a sphere increases towards the centre in proportion to the decrease in the surface on which it is applied.) The central particles will therefore be of much smaller volume and correspondingly of much greater density and will have a much faster internal movement. This gives the impression that the entire mass is concentrated in them, but this is not the case as the peripheral particles are also in contact with those at the centre and constantly exchanging movements with them. As a result of this cancelling out of movements, which is the fundamental phenomenon of the Universe, all the particles of the atom are of the same mass; they are not, however, all of the same volume. Consequently the equalization process is effected in the same way as between two wheels of different diameter: the smaller turns faster and the larger more slowly, the reduced speed of the latter being proportional to the size of its diameter (see Plate 7). This difference in motion gives the impression that the electron mass is 1,840 times smaller than that of the proton. It is also because the density of the electron is much more attenuated that the alpha particles are able to pass through it easily and not because the nucleus is surrounded by a vacuum, as Rutherford thought. Fuller details on this subject have been given elsewhere [2].

---

[1] *L'Univers en marche*, by Louis JACOT, Nouvelles Editions Latines, Paris.
[2] *Méditations sur le mouvement*, by Louis JACOT, Annex 2, Editions du Scorpion, Paris.

3. Shifting of material bodies

When a material body has to be moved, energy outside the body is brought into play. Two erroneous conclusions are drawn from this fact. The first is that the body to be shifted is inert or without movement; the second, that motion and matter are two different things. As a force exterior to an object is applied when that object is moved, it is assumed that the force is outside the object. As this force cannot be outside everything and the result of nothing, a convenient word, "energy", has been adopted and is defined as being the "ability" of a system of bodies to furnish "work". But this term "ability" gives rise to confusion. It assumes that a body can—in the case of an explosion, for example—produce movement by sleight of hand, drawing it out of nothing, as it were.

As soon as it is understood that the nature of matter is motion and that not only atoms but the particles that comprise them also have motion, it will be clear that when energy is produced, motion is not being created but only that a change of direction within matter has been effected. By transmitting surplus motion to a motion already in existence, its direction is modified and the position of an object in relation to its surroundings is accordingly changed. The impulsion transmitted to the bullet of a gun, for example, results in a modification in the quantity and direction of movement of the constituent particles of the bullet. It will be clear that this is so and that all particles participate in change of direction when a study is made of the effects produced on a group of people seated in a car which enters into collision with an obstacle and comes to a sudden stop. The passengers, to whom motion has been transmitted from particle to particle, are thrown forward violently in the direction of the original movement.

Material bodies are therefore not inert, that is to say, deprived of motion; if they do not shift in relation to each other without exterior influence, that is because, being all subjected to the same pressure by the ambiant medium, they all have the same dynamic resultant, which is that of the Earth through space. In fact, all material bodies are automobiles, at one and the same time propulsive and propulsed—propulsive because their constituent parts are moving, propulsed because an exterior motion transmitted to this interior movement shifts the material body in a continuation of the direction from which pressure is applied.

4. *Material and immaterial phenomena*

All material and immaterial phenomena are the result of motion and can only be explained by motion.

For example, the falling of bodies to the Earth is not the effect of the attraction at the centre of the Earth but of the concentric pressure of the ambiant medium which gives our planet its spherical form and maintains it in this form in spite of the extraordinary velocity at which it is moving on its orbit (30 km/sec). This is demonstrated by the fact that an object falling at the speed of a few metres a second at the same time as the Earth is advancing at the rate of 30 kilometres a second falls in the direction of the centre of the Earth. This would not happen if there was not an ambiant medium compressing the Earth and carrying it along. Chemical combinations are generally explained by what is called the "affinity" of certain bodies for others. But what is an affinity? Why does the combination of an acid and a base give a salt and water? The differences in the charge (positive or negative) which are supposed to be the determining factors in associations and dissociations in no way clarify the phenomenon if it is not examined on the basis of the motion that actuates the particles constituting the atoms.

The atoms, which are in effect sets of gears formed by particles in contact at their equators and through their poles, differ one from the other in the total number of particles of which they are comprised and in the manner in which these are fitted together. The various particle combinations give the atoms different structures. Being in motion and crowded together, the atoms are more likely to form more complex combinations when their structures complement each other, that is, offer the possibility of interlocking.

When the peripheral electrons form a compact surface without projections or cavities, the atoms do not couple. This is the case, in particular, with rare gas atoms such as neon, argon, krypton, etc. Their outer face, formed of eight peripheral elements, is complete and does not leave enough room for the electron of another atom to fit into it; for the same reason, as these eight peripheral electrons are so close together, none protrudes sufficiently to be able to fit into the electron hole of another atom.

But on the Earth, atoms with eight peripheral electrons are far fewer in number than those with less. When they have only 1, 2, 3, 4, 5, 6 or 7, they offer innumerable possibilities for coupling, this being more or less firm according to the structure in each case. Having examined this question elsewhere [1] with a number of supporting diagrams, no further details will be given here. Suffice it to note that the manner in which chemical combinations are formed is an irrefutable proof that the peripheral electrons are not "planetary" but are bound to given protons and consequently occupy fixed positions in the structure of the atom and are simultaneously being continuously actuated by their movement of rotation. A study of crystals—snow, for example, which is always hexagonal—confirms the conclusion that each atom has a structure similar to a set of gears in which each particle has its special place.

Once again the principle of the set of gears can be used to explain the nature of an electric current. It is generally described as a shifting of electrons in the heart of matter. This would

---

[1] *L'Univers en marche*, by Louis Jacot, Nouvelles Editions Latines, Paris.

imply continuous transmutation of the conductor wire, as the number of peripheral electrons of its atoms would be constantly altering. Such an explanation is obviously not valid. Furthermore, it is contradicted by the velocity of transmission which, in good conductors, is close to the velocity of light. The process by which electrons jump from one atom to another to take the place of those already there and propel them further is necessarily more time-consuming. But in a gear formation of moving particles, electricity is nothing but an acceleration of the motion transmitted from particle to particle, as in the case of the ripples in light phenomenon. The good conductors are the atoms with perfect gear formations, the bad conductors those with poor formations. In the latter case, surplus motion is badly transmitted as the particles which receive the surplus, without being able to retransmit it immediately, increase in size through the effect of the motion received, a calorific phenomenon being produced. Heat is, in fact, a bad transmission of motion, an electric current a good one.

As Faraday so superbly demonstrated, magnetic and electric phenomena are related; they are even interdependent. An electric current passing near a compass modifies the direction of the needle; conversely, a magnet brought near to, then withdrawn from, an electric coil produces a reversal of the current. As has already been mentioned elsewhere [1], these phenomena can only be explained if it is first accepted that particles in rotation exist, that they are in contact one with the other, and that they affect each other by their motion, as much at their equator as through their poles. Rotation has a "force" (or electric) nature at the equator and a "direction" (or magnetic) nature at the poles. The different directions of electromagnetic phenomena can be illustrated by the thumb and first two fingers of the left hand: the index pointing forward represents direction of current; the second

---

[1] *Méditations sur le mouvement*, by Louis JACOT, Annex 3 in particular—Observations on electromagnetism; Editions du Scorpion, Paris.

finger pointing perpendicularly in the horizontal represents direction of force; the thumb pointing perpendicularly in the vertical represents the magnetic field. This shows the interdependence of electricity and magnetism which are merely two aspects of the same phenomenon—a phenomenon which is nothing other than rotation, whether that of an elementary particle or of a celestial body, as terrestrial magnetism shows.

In view of the fact that all the particles of the Universe are in contact, magnetic phenomena are transmitted over great distances, those occurring on the sun producing serious disturbances on the Earth.

As the immaterial ether filling interstellar space is also formed of particles in rotation, it is understandable that magnetism is transmitted across space, each particle being a magnetic agent. As light is transmitted by means of such particles, it is also understandable that Maxwell thought of formulating an electromagnetic theory of light.

It is not possible to examine here the different theories on light. The subject is far too vast and has already been dealt with elsewhere [1] as well as in Chapter Six, Section 11, Subsection V above in relation to the age of the Earth. As was seen there, misunderstandings arose through the erroneous conceptions that prevailed regarding ether, which was presumed to be an inert and immobile fog through which the stars moved like automobiles. Ether, however, is not inert. On the contrary, it is dynamic. Neither is it immobile. It is ether itself that carries the celestial bodies along in their course, in particular the Earth around the sun. For this reason, Michelson's tests did not show a displacement of the Earth in relation to ether. The interferences that were expected did not take place and the entire theory of relativity, which is founded on this erroneous conception of ether, disqualifies itself [2].

---

[1] See previous works by the same author.

[2] *Méditations sur le mouvement*, by Louis JACOT, Annex 5, Editions du Scorpion, Paris.

Because it seemed to explain certain strange phenomena, the theory of relativity had many supporters, in spite of its threat to logic. For example, in an eclipse of the sun, the stars in its neighbourhood are not found in exactly the positions calculated by astronomers. Einstein concluded that the light rays emanating from them were "attracted" by the solar mass, which caused them to deviate from their paths. Now, as has been seen, there is no such thing as universal gravitation. If the stars are not in their expected positions, the explanation is as follows:

(1) In the heart of the solar vortex, ether particles are not everywhere of the same volume. Those near the centre are smaller and more dense. Light is necessarily transmitted faster through them than through the larger ones. At night, stars transmit their light rays only as far as the exterior limit of the terrestrial orbit. When, as happens on exceptional occasions such as an eclipse, they are visible during the day, their light rays also cross the entire diameter of the terrestrial orbit, that is, the region close to the sun where the particles are smaller and transmit the rays more rapidly.

(2) The solar vortex is not immobile. At the Earth's distance from the sun, it moves at the rate of 30 km/sec, and faster still at points closer to the sun. This velocity of the particles that transmit light should therefore be taken into consideration, either by addition or subtraction, according to whether the star is to the west or to the east of the sun and the light rays moving in the same direction as, or contrary to the direction of the vortex.

(3) Finally, the vortex motion necessarily produces deviation of light rays as the particles transmitting light move over large orbits, this deviation occurring not, as Einstein thought, in the direction of the sun but away from it.

5. *Evolution of matter*

The process of atom formation examined above does not correspond to the present stage in the evolution of the Universe, which is that of expansion, but to the previous stage of contraction.

Once the reversal of evolution occurred and expansion took the place of contraction, the constituent particles of the atom began to enlarge at the same time as all the ether particles. This general enlargement is at the root of the expansion of the Universe, conspicuous for the increase in the distances between the centres of the galaxies.

The expansion of particles is not the same everywhere in the Universe. Bode's law indicates that the centres of the vortexes are more compressed than the peripheral zones and that this expansion increases in accordance with a factor-2 geometric progression, starting at the centre and continuing until a certain outward distance has been reached. The atom particles of the Earth are governed by a similar type of expansion.

In the ligher atoms, that is, those formed by a relatively small number of particles, expansion is not spectacular. The situation is different in the case of complex atoms formed by a large number of helium atoms united through their poles and at their equators. Thrusting each against the other in their general expansion, they emit those alpha particles that are the least solidly incorporated in the overall structure. This constitutes the phenomenon of radioactivity. It is extremely important not only because it represents a danger to humanity, but also because it proves that the phenomenon of expansion not only governs the galaxies but extends its influence right down to the infinitesimally small and continuously transforms matter. It indicates that the atoms are veritable gear formations in which all particles are in contact. In a "planetary" system there would necessarily be a vacuum between the electrons and the protons; expansion in such circumstances would be absorbed by the vacuum and there would be no emission.

Universal expansion inevitably requires modification of the standards adopted for measuring space, time and the various material and immaterial phenomena. These standards are consequently not constant throughout the years. Furthermore, having been chosen more or less arbitrarily and without regard to evolution, they do not all change to the same extent. The space standard, for example, which was represented up to 31 December 1961 by a metallic bar and replaced as of 1 January 1962 by a length of a certain ray of the krypton atom, is involved in the evolution of the constituent particles of that atom. As to the time standard, it has been established as being that of a second in the year 1900. Theoretically it should not evolve as it is tied to a fixed date, but how can a time factor that occurred in 1900 be preserved? That is where the difficulties begin. However, this delicate problem has already been dealt with [1] and will not be enlarged on here.

In short, universal evolution involves not only that of matter but also of material and immaterial phenomena. It is absolutely essential that this fundamental truth be clearly understood when a standard is adopted or when those of different periods are used.

[1] *Eléments de physique évolutive*, by Louis JACOT, Editions du Scorpion Paris.

CHAPTER VIII

EVOLUTION OF LIFE

1. What is life?

Various theories have been put forward to explain life : animism is founded on an immaterial principle—the soul that animates the body; vitalism is based on a power of a special kind—the vital force; determinism is a physico-chemical doctrine—life is lodged in a particular state of matter, such as the colloidal state. But it is not by looking for an immaterial essence, a hidden force or a particular chemical substance that the secret of life will be discovered : life is not an independent "something", but a phenomenon.

Life is indissolubly linked with matter, which is motion. Life therefore cannot be anything else but motion. This in itself is already a very important discovery.

However, life cannot be compared to matter, as a clear distinction exists between living and dead matter. But in what does this distinction lie ? Certain viruses, such as those responsible for the tobacco illness called "mosaic", act exactly like living beings—assimilate substances and reproduce themselves—when they are in a suitable medium, whereas outside that medium they are in a crystal state. It was the American scientist, Stanley, who first demonstrated that it is possible to make this virus pass from the crystal to the living state. To avoid confusion, it must be mentioned right away that viruses develop only in a live medium. This test is nevertheless very interesting as it shows that chemical elements become living elements as soon as certain conditions allow them to participate in a cycle of operations consisting of the association of molecules, followed by their dissociation into fragments capable of recreating their original state by absorption of other molecules. Once this operation is terminated, the association gives place to a new dissociation, and so on. Absolutely identical chemical elements are therefore living elements when they take part in cyclic operations and nothing but simple crystals outside this cycle.

It is accordingly the cyclic movement, visible in this series of operations, that is characteristic of life, and a being can be said to be living when it constitutes an entity capable of ensuring the renewal of this cycle : the vital cycle.

Living beings therefore represent entities at a higher scale than that of material particles.

2. Requirements of life

The vital cycle is not a chain of operations that can be effected in a retort by a simple change in the state of a substance. The absorption of elements, in particular, constantly calls for the participation of exterior factors. A living entity is therefore very dependent on its environment, this dependence being not only voluntary and intermittent, but necessary and continuous, as certain phenomena, such as breathing, indicate. It is erroneous to consider life as being limited to a living entity when in fact it overflows into space as much as into time.

When the sequence in cyclic operations is broken, life ceases. The necessity of guaranteeing that the vital cycle is not interrupted involves, as a fundamental requirement, the creation of an organism, that is, of an entity capable of ensuring the repetition of the cycle. This entity is the cell.

The unicellular being therefore represents the smallest living entity, the "simplest" organism capable of ensuring the sequence of the cyclic operations without the assistance of other living beings (as is the case with the virus). A typical example of a unicellular being is the amœba.

This "simplest" organism is already extremely complex—just how complex can be gathered, up to a point, by examining its structure, multiple-inclusion cytoplasm, nucleus, pseudopodia, etc., under a microscope. But the most effective way of grasping its complexity is by visualizing the various functions it is called upon to carry out, i. e. change of position (if possible not too much at random) in order to find, seize and assimilate the elements it requires, produce enough energy for cellular activity, discard what is unsuitable, and finally split up into each of its constituent parts in order to form two daughter cells. The technical problems raised by each of these operations, and the latter's coordination in a single unit, are striking proofs of the extraordinary perfection of such an organism.

In spite of this, the unicellular being is limited in its exercise of these many complex functions. Mobility, so important for obtaining indispensable elements, raises problems that can only be very imperfectly solved by a single cell. The same applies to assimilation of such elements. These, more often than not, are in forms that cannot be absorbed until they have been transformed, etc., etc. In short, the problems raised by these functions can only be suitably solved by the creation of multicellular, that is, still more complex, beings.

3. Complexity of life

Multicellular beings differ from the unicellular more by the specialization of their activities than by their number, the cells generally being grouped as organs, each carrying out a specific function : locomotion, seizing of food, digestion, respiration, secretion, coordination, etc.

This specialization is of considerable advantage. Development and improvement of the organs enable the being to move with more facility in its environment, change position with more speed and over greater distances, carry more easily what it needs, contribute to the production of what suits it best, recognize what is useful and avoid what is detrimental. Certain organs constitute real laboratories in which are secreted any number of products required for the transformation and assimilation of elements ; others, even more complex, are responsible for coordinating all these activities.

But specialization also has its inconveniences, even serious ones : most of the cells cannot move about freely in the nutritional medium in order to obtain what is essential to their life and, even worse, they are no longer able to divide. These are two obstacles of a technical nature arising from the impossibility of exercising simultaneously activities that are too dissimilar. (The same instrument is not used to play the violin and to wash dishes !) Organs can only function if the cells are in contact and if their structure corresponds to their activity, but once cells are grouped into an organ—the heart, for example, or the eye—they can no longer divide and at the same time carry out their specific activity. In short, specialization is the cause of these two obstacles. Now the vital cycle consists as much in absorption of elements as in cellular division. Specialization therefore raises two problems that have to be solved if the cycle is to continue.

Nature solved the first in the most faultless manner by simply reversing it. Instead of the cell moving about in the nutritional medium, the medium itself, by means of specialized organs, irrigates all the cells of an entity, either in the form of sap, lymph or blood.

The solution to the second problem was less satisfactory. As functional activity prevented cellular division, and as cellular division was one of the fundamental operations of the vital cycle, Nature made a choice. Certain cells, the specialized ones, were sacrificed in favour of the non-specialized ones which, however, were capable of division and of separating themselves from the individual entity, thereby ensuring reproduction. As to the specialized cells, they no longer exercised a complete function of their own to the extent that the vital cycle consisting of absorption and cellular division was replaced by a series of absorption and secretion operations that ensured the one function. However, as cellular division was thereby excluded, complete regeneration was necessarily also excluded and the cell and the organ to which it belonged were subject to the ageing process. On the other hand, the cells that were not tied down to functional activities (apart from that of reproduction) created, by means of the dividing process, two groups of cells, one designed to specialize and form the organs (and accordingly destined to die), the other (non-specialized) to ensure the continuation of life by dividing into two.

The multicellular being is therefore the result of a compromise as it is only multicellular (up to the time of its death) as concerns the solution of various problems, such as those of feeding, and remains unicellular for the purpose of ensuring reproduction by cellular division.

This does not mean that the multicellular being does not enter into the reproductive process. On the one hand, by its activity it feeds the reproductive cells and is therefore their preserver and multiplier; on the other, as it is capable of contracting certain illnesses, these can be transmitted to the reproductive cells, kill them or prevent them from dividing normally; it can therefore also be their destroyer. When the multicellular being dies, the reproductive cells that are dependent on it also die.

The multicellular being plays yet another part in sexual reproduction: as cellular division is subject to a certain determinism to the extent that that which divides is something that exists and not something that doesn't, an alteration in the composition of a cell inevitably leads to a corresponding modification in the structure of the daughter-cells. To compensate for the degeneration that such changes could produce, Nature has devised a very ingenious process whereby special cellular division, or meiosis, produces two half-cells only capable of reproducing themselves if each is united to the half cell of another individual. The union of these two half cells or gametes—the male called the spermatozoid, the female, the ovulum—produces the egg cell in which another multicellular being is created. Sexual reproduction is nevertheless not confined to multicellular beings; it also occurs from time to time in unicellular beings, particularly when the medium in which they live is not renewed sufficiently frequently to enable each cell to obtain all of the elements it requires. This demonstrates once again the complexity of unicellular beings.

The union of the male and female gametes must take place in a favourable medium. In the case of fish, it can occur simply in the water, where the egg is transformed into an individual multicellular entity without the participation of the parents. In the case of numerous animals, the egg can only develop suitably in the body of an adult, where favourable conditions of temperature and feeding are guaranteed. This requirement is at the root of the sexual act.

Numerous multicellular beings are incapable of developing by their own means in the period following birth. In the case of the mammals, the mother suckles her young for a certain time, and in numerous other species the parents take care of their offspring up to the time they become adult.

Various insects—bees, ants, termites, etc.—form colonies of beings with different functions, reproduction being the responsibility of a female who lays a large number of eggs while the task of fertilizing them falls to one or more males. A mass of workers carry out the functions of looking for food, constructing and defending the shelter, ventilating it, taking care of the larva, etc. In such cases, the actual living entity is the colony as a whole and not the individual which, in spite of its mobility, operates as nothing more than an organ. When the queen of a hive dies, the other bees cease all activity and very quickly die too.

All this indicates that the vital problems are extremely complex. The difficulty begins as soon as it has to be decided whether phenomena are vital or simply physico-chemical as, life being a cycle, the former are in fact only part of a sequence that includes the latter. New difficulties arise as soon as an attempt is made to follow the various stages of an individual entity. A unicellular being very quickly divides and consequently no longer exists as an entity; a multicellular being, produced by a unicellular organism, becomes multicellular only temporarily in order to reproduce itself in the form of unicellular beings. By sexual reproduction, a being does not have one ancestor, but two parents, four grandparents, etc. It is therefore impossible to decide what is particular to each individual, as much in the ascending as the descending line, over a number of generations. And this is no easier, incidentally, with the unicellular beings as the parents cease to exist as parents and, after dividing, they become their own offspring.

The complexity of vital phenomena assumes unsuspected proportions as soon as the relations between individual beings are fairly closely studied. Those that feed solely on inorganic, i.e. purely chemical, elements are in the minority. The majority feed on other living beings, vegetable or animal, which disappear as entities on becoming incorporated in them. The use of previously transformed material—that is, the absorption of one living being by another—simplifies considerably the problem of assimilation. It is therefore very widespread on our planet.

The excretions and carcasses of living beings on the Earth would long ago have become extremely encumbering if it were not that others get rid of them by absorbing them. Nature's garbage disposal and utilization of waste service is more important than generally supposed as without it the accumulation of decaying matter would soon have prevented the spread of life on Earth.

The plants that draw nourishment from organic substances in decomposition are called saprophytes and, in fact, are in the majority. In symbiosis, various beings club together in order to live, each deriving benefit from this association, whereas in parasitism one lives at the expense of the other. The latter is also very widespread.

In short, the vital phenomenon is extraordinarily complex. It is therefore advisable to consider it as a whole in order to assess it adequately. If it is better, from a pedagogical point of view, to study living beings from different angles—anatomy, physiology, embryology, etc.—the overall picture of the vital phenomenon should not be lost sight of as the life of highly developed individuals such as Man is only possible in the context of interdependent phenomena. This shows that all living beings on our planet are at one and the same time interdependent and mutually supporting and that everything has a role to play, including excretions and corpses.

4. Evolution of life

Life, a phenomenon closely associated with matter, can obviously not escape the evolutionary process which, as has been seen, manifests itself by an expansion of all the particles of universal substance. The molecules that form living beings consequently grow through the years. Nevertheless, this expansion does not seem to have too wide an effect as it is minimal in the period of time covered by the life of an individual and only results in disintegration in the case of very complex bodies, said to be radioactive, which do not form part of the composition of living beings, at any rate not on our planet. Nevertheless, although scarcely perceptible at Man's scale of daily observations, this expansion is of great significance as it shows that the very root of life is change and that nothing stable and permanent can be constructed on this basis. Only something that evolves can be built up on something evolving. Life, in short, is nothing but a second-degree evolution, the first being material evolution.

The effects of universal evolution are not seen only in the expansion of particles. By modifying the rotation and translation conditions of the Earth, evolution also caused changes in climate with all their consequences—glaciations, variations in sea level—

and orogenic movements that produced upheavals and sometimes assumed catastrophic proportions.

Life was only able to survive during such adverse occurrences thanks to a capacity of adaptation which was all the more remarkable in that it appears to have preceded the events. It is certain that the evolutionary process did not continue to develop through the medium of carcasses after a catastrophe had occurred. Just as animals migrate before conditions unfavourable to them arise and the embryo develops organs it is only destined to use after birth, so evolution appears to have prepared the species for each change in condition.

This capacity of adaptation (and of pre-adaptation) is the main feature of the vital phenomena. As it constitutes the root of evolution of the species, it can also be observed in the evolution of individuals (healing of wounds, immunity phenomena, muscular development through training, etc.).

Nevertheless, evolution of the individual is not governed solely by adaptation, at least not in the way the individual would like, as it results in ageing and death. The question of whether these disadvantages are avoidable or not is frequently raised. As all cells are irrigated and receive the necessary material for their activity, it could be expected that this supply would regenerate them continuously. In fact, as soon as organs begin to function, an ageing process is observable in the form of wear and tear, deposits, hardening, slowing down of activity, etc. This phenomenon seems to be the result of the functional activity itself which keeps the cells in contact and prevents them from dividing, as already mentioned. Cellular division appears to be the only technical means of ensuring lasting life. Death is therefore the result of the specialization that prevents division.

To compensate for death, Nature has given superior beings, especially Man, the possibility of making life deeper, fuller, richer than unicellular life. This advantage is, however, only relative for the majority of individuals, who put their capabilities to the worst possible use. Yet in spite of everything, and even though it leads to the death of the multicellular individual, evolution of life has its justification as it is able to produce a blooming of the personality through an awakening of conscience which is in fact the only real reason for existence. Unfortunately, Man generally arrives at an awareness of himself and of the meaning of life only at the moment he leaves it.

The evolution of the species, which would be completely incomprehensible if it were assumed that the Earth had been subject in the past to the same conditions as those of the present time, assumes its full significance as soon as the successive changes in conditions are followed through the ages. This evolution was without doubt a continuous process of adaptation to exterior conditions and a close study of these is indispensable if the evolutionary process is to be understood; conversely, a study of evolution enables exterior conditions to be reconstructed.

It is unfortunately not known how these transformations were effected. At the present time the egg cell of a species automatically develops in such a way as to produce an individual similar to the one from which the cell came. Conditions are such at the moment that no evolution in this process is required. Consequently, as it is not possible to compare a known with an unknown phenomenon, there is no alternative but to remain in ignorance.

Another reason for this lack of knowledge is that the problem is generally badly approached. Even if the global phenomenon of evolution of the species is not visibly taking place, information is available in the partial and significant phenomena that occur daily, such as the metamorphosis of certain insects, development of embryos, psychical and physical interdependence, etc. But with all this partial knowledge, it is still not possible to reconstruct global phenomenon because the entire science of biology is vitiated by an absurd dilemma created by the simple-minded who insist that the explanation of life is either purely mechanical—implying that matter is at the root of everything and that the phenomenon is therefore due to chance—or based on a certain organization leading to a given end. In the latter context, there is talk about finality, and as this word has been given a divine connotation, everything that occurs in the Universe is attributed to Divine Will.

It would be foolish to deny that eyes are created for seeing, legs for walking, wings for flying, the digestive system for digesting, lungs for breathing, etc. The word "organ" implies an organization created for a purpose. Obviously, a system as complex and incredibly perfect as a cell is no more the result of chance than a jet aircraft or an atomic bomb. This does not mean that the aircraft of the bomb are of divine creation.

It is sheer intellectual laziness to attribute to God or to chance what cannot be explained. This lack of understanding results from a total ignorance of the phenomenon of thought. Man considers that animals are inferior to him. Accordingly, when he observes birds building their nests and spiders weaving their webs, as he is incapable of imitating them, he claims that they are acting in accordance with "instinct" or else he uses other terms, popular with scientists, who substitute labels for what they cannot explain. Man's claim to a monopoly of intelligence prevents him from recognizing that all vital phenomena are related to thought as much as to matter ; he thereby demonstrates his exceptional lack of intelligence.

Since the extraordinary advances made in the technical field, there is a tendency in broad scientific circles to consider science as being only truly scientific if human thought is excluded. This is a serious matter.

Instead of deforming problems by hemming them in with inept dilemmas that create prejudice, it would be wiser to start by considering what constitutes thought.

CHAPTER IX

EVOLUTION OF THOUGHT

1. What is thought?

As matter is motion, as life is motion, can thought, which is closely linked to life, be anything but motion? Obviously not.

But then what does this motion, called thought, consist of? Why is it linked to life? What is the nature of this link? In what way does the motion called thought resemble that of life and in what way does it differ?

To summarize once again the characteristics of the motion that actuates matter: there is within the elementary particle a movement of rotation that evolves and thereby causes the particle to expand at its equator and flatten at its poles. This rotary movement is at the root of electromagnetism, as already shown in Chapter Seven, Section 4. Electricity and magnetism are therefore merely two complementary aspects of the same phenomenon, electricity being the "force" aspect and magnetism the "direction". It is impossible to separate one from the other as there cannot be force without direction or direction without force. As Faraday demonstrated, magnetism produces electricity—electricity, magnetism.

The movement that grafts itself on that of matter and constitutes life inevitably also has two aspects, those of "force" and of "direction". "Force" is the vital activity, "direction" nothing other than thought.

Thought is, in short, a certain facet of a global phenomenon. Sentiments as much as ideas "direct" vital activities.

The term "direction" also implies sequence as it is by following the direction of a motion that its series of connections can be seen, the first part generally being termed cause and the second effect. One individual is more intelligent than another when he is capable of following this chain of cause and effect further; logic is precisely the art of putting together these links.

Sensations record the contacts established with the exterior world, that is, with other motions, their force and direction. This recording constitutes an act of awareness which is only possible when a motion that catches up with itself is perturbed. Actually an act of awareness requires the coexistence of several circular motions which affect, and consequently exert mutual control on each other. Now, the vital phenomena are precisely cyclic motions superimposed on the circular movement of material particles. Inside a cell there are numerous movements that combine and make of the cell not only a living but also a thinking entity.

It may seem bold to consider the cell, which constitutes the basis of vegetable as much as animal life, a thinking entity. This implies that a tree is a thinking being. But the habit of ascribing everything to Man and considering him as the standard of all phenomena should not be allowed to lead to error. A tree heals its wounds, and this is something that no machine can do. Admittedly, it is done in accordance with a certain mechanism to which an "ism" term can be applied in lieu of an explanation, but that does not justify a tree being compared to a machine. A process of adaptation, which is the general phenomenon of Nature, is in fact manifest. Plants have roots, stems, leaves, flowers and fruit but the relation between these different organs is neither rigid nor fixed. If young plants are placed in very favourable soil, from which they can draw nourishment without difficulty, they grow well and quickly, but the roots remain small. If, on the contrary, the soil is arid, the roots develop considerably. Similar cases of adaptation are numerous. Young strawberry plants have been placed in arid 5-cm-thick ground above a very rich mould. All the plants developed, from the cervix, a long taproot, 5 cms in length, at the end of which sprang the root. Adaptation took the form of organization.

The absence, in the vegetable world, of a nervous system similar to that found in the animal kingdom and the smaller cerebral development of the latter compared to Man should not lead to facile conclusions and to the assumption that thought only exists at the level of an algebraic formula. Life and thought are as inseparable as electricity and magnetism. All living things, therefore, participate in thought. The only difference between the species is one of degree.

The custom of regarding thought as something abstract should not encourage the belief that thought takes place in a void. There are always connected movements at the root of all reasoning. The claim that $2 + 2 = 4$ is nothing but the confirmation of biological phenomena of which one link in the series is being considered.

The fact that Man is capable of developing a thought, that is, of noticing direction and connection and consequently the relationship between cause and effect, does not mean that he has "invented" thought or that he is the only living being in whom the power to think has been lodged. He has not created thought and when he uses it he is not drawing it out of the void but merely profiting from an organ which enables him to develop and exploit a phenomenon that is present in the entire living world at the cellular level.

Although life is observable in the individual, whether uni- or multicellular, it overflows as much into time as into space. It cannot be otherwise, as thought is only one aspect of vital activity. The close and permanent relationship between the individual and his environment can be noted daily by the infectiousness of laughter, anger, etc. The phenomena of adaptation to emotional atmosphere—music for example—are too well known to be repeated here. In the manifestations of a crowd—its excitement, frenzy, anger, panic—individual thought is completely subjected to collective thought. Immediate adaptation is obvious.

Just as motion (particularly expansion) in the smallest material particle existing on the Earth is conditioned by the overall motion of the Universe, not only in the infinitesimally small but in the infinitely large (withdrawal of the galaxies), so are the phenomena of life and thought on our planet subordinate to all the motions of the Universe. Admittedly, movements in the immediate environment exercise greater influence than those further removed, but interdependence is nevertheless total from one end of the Universe to the other, as demonstrated in particular by the sun's magnetic storms, the effects of which reach as far as the Earth. Not only do they perturb radiogoniometric apparatus but completely put birds in flight off their course. And this is quite understandable. As all living beings are formed of particles in rotation, they all have their own magnetism which is not only influenced by that of the environment but cannot avoid being in consonance with it.

Our planet is not an isolated celestial body governed by special laws. It is part of a whole and is interpenetrated and dominated by it. True, each celestial body is exposed to conditions of its own according to its individual position, which is never the same as that of any other body. This influences its material and life evolution. But all celestial bodies are subject to the general laws of motion which are the same in every part of the Universe, and all are influenced by the motions in their immediate neighbourhood.

The same holds true for the individual. Constituted of particles individually actuated by movement and collectively grouped into sets with motions superimposed at the scale of the atom, molecule, cell and organ, the individual represents a complex of interdependent movements, the balance of which is necessary for the maintenance of life. Once the coexistence and super-imposition of these myriad intricate movements inside the individual and their mutual influence are grasped, it is easy to realize that disorders can occur at various levels and require different kinds of medical treatment. In addition to the classical methods taught in Western colleges, Chinese acupuncture, chiropractice, magne-tism, autosuggestion, hypnosis, witchcraft, etc., can give results, as all of these techniques are designed to modify the relative balance of these various movements. The influence of the mental on the physical and vice versa also becomes easy to comprehend ; they are but two aspects of the same global phenomenon. The part played by the surrounding medium is considerable as the perturbations occurring in it modify the movements of the elemen-tary particles, in particular their direction, and inevitably affect all the internal movements of the individual. As the disturbances caused by magnetic storms show, there is in fact a permanent "direction" relationship between the living being and the Cosmos.

Study of the individual shows that thought is the creation of the thinker. Evolution of the species shows that the thinker is a product of thought. Is one of these concepts more valid than the other ? Are they contradictory ? Or should it not rather be considered that thinker and thought are one ? They can, in fact only be distinguished as separate concepts if the observation of a global phenomenon is limited to one or to the other. Making a distinction between the two appears to be logical as the thinker is regarded as being concrete and existing in his own right while thought appears to be abstract, i.e., a phenomenon. But actually the living being formed of particles in motion is also a pheno-menon—a phenomenon of longer duration than a thought but a phenomenon nevertheless, arising from motion.

Matter, life and thought are all aspects of universal motion. Only an obstinate and small-minded prejudice regarding the superiority of Man and of our planet prevents recognition of the fact that matter, life and thought are universal and that their study can only be adequately carried out in the context of the Universe as a whole.

2. Evolution of thought through the ages

A quick glance at the evolution of the species shows that this process consisted in an adaptation of life to changing conditions. By displacing their habitat, certain marine species managed to remain in waters whose composition and temperature altered very little. This displacement was generally effected in a direction contrary to the Earth's rotation, the species in this way remaining constantly in the same position in relation to the sun. This was also possible for certain groups of marine plants, when rotation was very slow. In their case, evolution through the ages did not take place.

The situation was quite different for other species, land types in particular, their westward migrations being halted by the seas; the marine species of inland waters encountered the same problem when they reached land. It was a question of: evolve or die.

As conditions on Earth in former times were quite different from those of today, evolution was not confined solely to adaptation to changes of temperature, involving changes of food in the animal world. Neither in the Archean age nor in the Primary era does the Earth appear to have had a layer of oxygenized air such as is known at the present time. Animals similar to the species of today could therefore not have existed. Those exposed to solar radiation were protected by scales, even the fish being similarly armoured. There was a period of half-water half-land life conspicuous for the dipnoan, a fish capable of adapting itself to various environments thanks to gills and an air bladder that could be transformed into lungs. Then came the amphibia. It is likely that the atmosphere at the time of the lush Carboniferous vegetation was overloaded with carbonic gas as it was subsequent to this period of extraordinary plant life (in which enormous quantities of oxygen must have been liberated) that the continents appear to have become really habitable for the vertebrata. The monsters of the Secondary era, many of which still had bony scales, were of inordinate size, some as much as 25 metres in length and weighing more than 25 tons. The fact that they were able to devour up to 300 kilos of foodstuff in a day indicates that there must have been at that time an extraordinary plant life, enriching the atmosphere in oxygen and rarefying it. In this connection, it must be remembered that flowering plants first appeared in the Cretaceous period, at the end of the Secondary era. This was probably connected with a change in the composition of the Earth's atmosphere.

The appearance of mammalia in the Tertiary era marks an important stage in evolution as the necessity for the mother to suckle her young and take care of them during a relatively long period of time appears to correspond not to an adaptation to climatic changes—other classes of vertebrata or invertebrata were not subject to this modification—but to some internal evolution. On the basis of more and more advanced specialization—this is the case with the change from reptiles to birds—the evolutionary process in the mammalia appears to have taken the form of development of the cerebral system, a more complete and therefore slower development.

The human species were the last to appear and, so far, represent the highest stage in this development. Their offspring take the longest time to become independent.

Evolution, therefore, has attained, in the human species, a broadening and deepening of thought.

3. Evolution of human thought

Man differs from the other animals in his mental development, which appears to have evolved from the earliest known genus (Pithecanthropus and Sinanthropus). This is not the place to discuss whether these should be classified in the human species or in the category of sub-human anthropoids. Many excellent works are available on the subject. What must be emphasized here is that unquestionable morphological evolution took place from these primitive types onwards (cranial capacity, particular features (facial angle, etc.)) and justifies the assumption that there has been a process of continuous development in the physiological output of the brain, that is, in intelligence (see Plate 6). It should be noted, however, that successive human types differed only in degree and not in nature; the same applies, incidentally, as between primitive man and the other animals (monkeys in particular) and, as already seen in the previous section, as between the animal and vegetable world.

It is very difficult to decide exactly which type of primitive man corresponds to what is termed pretentiously (or ironically) "homo sapiens"; it is still more difficult when Man of the present day is observed where considerable differences are noticeable, not only as far as the morphology of the skull is concerned, but also the degree of civilization. It should be borne in mind that during the greater part of the Quaternary era, with its series of glaciations and inter-glaciations, life was very difficult not only because of changes of climate but also because of their extremes. Civilization, however, can only develop in the context of a certain stability. There were consequently no great civilizations prior to the stabilization of climates.

Noticeable progress was made as concerns the invention of early tools and the production of fire; after chipped stone came polished stone, then the use of metals, development of pottery, construction of huts, domestication of animals and agriculture.

In historic times, that is, from about 3,500 B.C., several remarkable civilizations sprang up in Mesopotamia, Egypt, China, India, Crete, Greece, Asia Minor, etc. They are noteworthy not only for the superb works of art they left behind but even more for the awakening of consciousness that they represent.

They reflect Man's will to improve and his realization that this is only possible through collaboration and solidarity.

The destruction of these civilizations also shows that advances in thought and awareness of human solidarity were far from being the attribute of all men, the noblest efforts generally being brought to naught by the megalomania and tyranny of rulers. All great conquerors were great destroyers. In the final analysis, even Alexander the Great, who had been brought up on the philosophy of Aristotle, succeeded only in annihilating the genius of Greece and Persia. The Romans undertook to do the rest.

It is not in men such as these that the constructors of human thought will be found, but in the wise men of all ages who, through deep meditation, arrived at an awareness of themselves and of the world in which they lived. Each achieved this end in his own fashion. Buddha concentrated on the problem of suffering and built up his religion on the conclusions to which this led him. Here was an extraordinary awakening of conscience, and since Buddha, strangely enough, this problem has not been carried much further. Admittedly, various methods of combatting pain have now been invented, but the fundamental problem of pain itself has been completely ignored. And yet this is a field in which developments of the highest interest are still to be made. Socrates, Plato, Aristotle and all the Pleiad of great Greek philosophers who preceded or followed them tried to arrive at an awareness of themselves and of the world as much by study of fundamental problems, such as that of motion, as by a heightened introspection. So aware was Christ of Man's solidarity that he never ceased preaching brotherly love. While the Greeks sought improvement through reasoning, Christ pursued the same ends through the emotions. The work of St. Augustine is another awakening of conscience and his attempt to construct the City of God was founded as much on reasoning as on the emotions. The Renaissance marked a new advance in Man's awareness, frontiers being extended in space and in time. The work of earlier philosophers was revived and at the same time Copernicus and Galileo arrived at a more precise idea of the world through study of the skies and reflections regarding the occurrences noted there.

Then came Descartes, who rid himself of all the out-dated concepts with which he had been crammed and replaced them by new ideas, but only after having satisfied himself as to their veracity. This method introduced the new way of thinking of modern times—or rather what should be, as there is, in fact, as much difference between a Cartesian and Descartes as between a Christian and Christ.

Unfortunately, since Descartes and the beginning of the Age of Reason, Man has not become more reasonable for all of that and the horrible massacres in which this generation has participated, either as witness, victim or executioner, do not encourage a very high opinion of Man's improvement. The worst is that this experience has not been of any use and today, as yesterday, Ministers of State only think in terms of striking force and subordinate all their politics to this obsession. Striking force is the force of the weak-minded, in whom pride and the necessity to dominate have produced one aim only, to the exclusion of all others: to prove their superiority—to the point of becoming supremely stupid. Admittedly, there is no question of adopting a wide-eyed pacifism and of assuming that it is enough not to attack to be safeguarded against attack. The entire history of humanity proves the contrary and should be an inducement to prudence and foresight. But it is not by pretending to be superior to others that cooperation between more or less civilized nations, which is the only way of avoiding war, will be established.

This should not constitute cause for despair. Man's awakening of conscience has made real progress in various directions during modern times. Rousseau's "Social Contract", for example, brought to the fore the principles of individual liberty and equality at a moment when there was only question of social classes and privileges. His ideas fomented numerous revolutions and continue to be of influence. Henry Dunant, deeply affected by the horror of war, managed to create a movement of opinion which led to the foundation of the Red Cross and to a respect for the most elementary principles of humanity being imposed on governments. In the scientific field, the work of Pasteur, by revealing a completely unknown facet of the living world and at the same time producing the means of combatting the gravest illnesses, represents an awakening of conscience that has transformed and regenerated life.

The idea of Man's solidarity has made real progress. It has even led to the creation of various international organizations which, though responsible for much nonsense, can nevertheless be (and certainly will be) improved as soon as they decide not to carry into the supranational milieu the unfortunate behaviour of their own Ministers of State. In order to avoid future catastrophes due to the stupidity of politicians, certain over-simplified projects envisage the creation of vast super-States. These will obviously be good for business, but that, after all, is not society's only problem. Humanity is composed of individuals, family groups, town and country communities, cantons, provinces, etc., forming national states. These subdivisions of society are designed to solve community problems at various levels, but it is not by abolishing the levels that the problems will be abolished as well (particularly if large national blocks are created), or that politicians will become wiser.

Of course the most elementary prudence makes it necessary to avoid complacent optimism. Experience has shown that technical progress is generally harnessed by governments to destructive ends. The well-being that scientific development has contributed to humanity is continuously being sapped by this category of super-men, thanks to whom politics has become the art of resolving minor difficulties by transforming them into absolutely insolvable major problems. But there is still room for hope. Ministers of State need accomplices for the execution of their crimes. Now, although these political giants themselves are not to be convinced, since neither logic nor morals enters into their considerations, this is not so of public opinion. Rousseau and Dunant were not official personalities and yet their ideas spread to such an extent that they compelled recognition, first by the public, then by governments. Real force is not striking force but force of mind that looks for truth, discovers it little by little, and diffuses it widely. Mind, in the final analysis, controls the world and leads it forward.

There are good reasons for supposing that the world is on the threshold of a new renaissance, much vaster and more significant than the movement to which this term is generally applied, and this in spite of the fact that men are, for the most part, still like a large flock of sheep, transformed into wolves for the purpose of killing, reverting to their sheep-like nature again and being killed, vacillating between the pack and the flock. There is still much to be done before society becomes a society of real men. The hardest fight is against the mentality of those who are suspicious of ideas, who claim to be "practical", who only accept what they call "facts". For all those (and for the fools amongst them) who think that "things being what they are", the acme of intelligence consists in pursuing the path of routine and corruption. Humanity needs an intellectual, spiritual and moral revolution and events seem to be moving in this direction.

Every day the frontiers of the unknown are being pushed further and further back by scientific discoveries that give to Man the possibility of enlarging his horizons and of understanding himself more completely. Grasping the truth, he will at last be able to take his own measure, assess the world in which he lives, and understand the process of evolution and the part he can and must play in it. Such a powerful, deep and widespread awakening of consciousness in time and in space, covering the past and the future and giving all its fullness to the present, can become the basis of an entirely new Humanism.

CHAPTER X

CONCLUSIONS

The idea of evolution has made considerable progress in recent years. Nevertheless, if it has carried all before it in certain fields of science, it is only tolerated in others side by side with the idea of permanency. Astronomers accept the fact that the galaxies are speeding away and consequently evolving but at the same time cling to their ideas on the permanency of the solar system; physicists simultaneously support the theory of evolution of matter, as manifested in radiation and radioactivity, and that of inertia, which again implies permanency.

The concept of evolution, however, tolerates no compromise. In no circumstances can it admit a contradiction, such as that of permanency, as it is based on the principle that evolution is the result of motion and that everything in the Universe is motion, down to the elementary particles that constitute matter and fill inter-stellar space. Neither can it accept the notion that one part of the Universe evolves and that another part is permanent; that some celestial bodies are evolving and others are immutable; that certain material bodies are subject to transformation whilst others remain stable. All particles of the Universe, material and immaterial, are in motion and have no properties other than those of motion. Motion is consequently the very essence of the Universe, which cannot be other than dynamic.

The differences between the various elements constituting matter (electrons, protons, etc.) are due purely to differences in conditions of movement (direction, position in the general structure and consequently, pressure).   These differences lead to the assumption that the immaterial particles filling inter-stellar space are different from material particles.   This is not so.   All have the same nature—motion.

Evolution involves a way of thinking so different from the traditional manner of considering any subject that a precise idea of the world will only be obtained if, following strictly Descartes' fundamental rule, the board is cleared of all preconceptions (permanency, inertia, universal gravitation, etc.) and Man's entire body of knowledge reconstructed solely on the basis of what has been proven to be true.

Evolution permeates the entire Universe from the infinitesimally small to the infinitely large, galactic expansion being nothing but the sum of the expansion of all elementary particles.

Expansion of particles produces evolution of material bodies, the most spectacular effect of which is radioactivity.   Evolution is also constantly modifying the position and movements of the celestial bodies.   Grouped in systems that grow from day to day, they are subject to irrevocable change, affecting as much their size as their translation and rotation.   Nothing is less exact than to take it for granted that the Earth has always had days of 24 hours and years of 365 days.   Evolution modifies standards of time as much as of space.

As the intrinsic nature of the Universe is motion, everything that is considered to be "real", such as matter, is in fact nothing more than a phenomenon.   If this phenomenon appears to be permanent and to exist outside motion, that is partly because the circular movement that actuates its particles is so rapid that it gives the illusion of stability, partly because the time available to Man for his observations is too short to enable the evolution of matter, in the form of expansion, to be directly perceptible except through certain effects, such as radioactivity.   Matter is a phenomenon that is nonetheless unfolding before the eyes of all.   Actually matter as such does not exist—only material phenomena.   Similarly life as such, thought as such, do not exist—only vital and psychical phenomena.

In the Universe where all is motion and where all the particles—which are motion—are in contact, everything is interdependent, movement being transmitted from particle to particle in the same way as saw-toothed wheels in gear. This interdependence in time and space is so vast that no single unit in the Universe can be isolated. Consequently, to be suitably solved, all problems must be examined from three aspects: the first, that of the unit under study (in particular its internal movement, especially that of its constituent parts); the second, that of its connection with the overall system (in particular with universal evolution); the third, that of its relationship with its neighbours (including the special conditions of the latter, particularly when the unit in question forms, with these neighbours, a larger entity).

This procedure makes it possible to avoid misunderstandings, such as those of physicists who have established the age of the Earth at several milliard years. This has given Man an erroneous sense of security, leading him to suppose that evolution is, if not terminated, at least without practical consequences, that for millions and milliards of years the Earth will remain more or less as it is today, and that no significant changes will ever take place. Our study of evolution has shown, on the contrary, that the evolutionary process in fact never stops, that it continuously unrolls at a giddy pace and that it subjects all celestial bodies to conditions that are very difficult indeed and that cannot be avoided by our planet. In spite of these trials, Man has, to a considerable extent, the possibility of being the artificer of his destiny. He would be wise to awake at last to a consciousness of the world in which he lives, understand that he is faced with far more serious problems than international or ideological squabbles, and consider the necessary steps to be taken for his safety if he wishes to avoid ending up like the dinosaur.

REMARKS CONCERNING THE ILLUSTRATIONS

The following plates are more than illustrations of a text; they are all subjects for deep meditation. Although there are not many of them, they should lead all thinking persons to realize that evolution is a universal phenomenon occurring everywhere and at all times; that it is not limited to the past but continues in the present and will continue on into the future; that it is not confined to certain places or certain objects; that it is not a random occurrence that might perhaps or might not affect permanency.

Evolution and permanency are incompatible. To understand this, it is enough to study the causes and mechanism of the former As soon as the dynamic nature of the elementary particles and the effect they have on each other are recognized (see Plates 7 and 8), it has to be acknowledged that permanency has no place in the Universe, the fundamental phenomenon of which is evolution.

Plates 1 to 6 are designed to show the universal character of evolution, Plates 7 and 8, its mechanism, the last seven, the evolution of the Earth in particular.

An examination of the various aspects of evolution will give the reader who takes the trouble to ponder over the series of "Whys?" the possibility of acquiring an exact and at the same time fantastic idea of the destiny of the Universe. By raising himself to its scale, he will arrive at a true awareness of himself and of his relations with the world in which he lives.

Plate 1 : *Evolution of the galaxies.*

Four examples of spiral nebulae chosen from many.   Top left : M 51 ; top right : NGC 4736 ; both in the Hunting Dogs.   Bottom left : the Great Nebula of Andromeda ; bottom right : M 101 in the Big Bear.

Mount Wilson photographs.

These photographs supply vivid pictures of universal evolution.

Subjects for thought.

1. The entire Universe is in motion.
2. The galaxies are actuated by overall motion involving not only all the celestial bodies of which they are composed but all matter existing in inter-stellar space.
3. As a result of their rotary motion, the galaxies are deformed, becoming more and more flattened and progressively expanding. This expansion of the diameter of each galaxy leads to the general expansion of the Universe manifested by increasing distance between all visible galactic centres, thus giving the impression that the galaxies are speeding away from one another.
4. Centrifugal force within a rotating galaxy is responsible for the expulsion of a part of the mass, as is so strikingly seen in the superb satellite at the bottom of the spiral arm of M 51.
5. The spiral form is unstable and testifies to the speed of evolution.

Plate 2 : *Evolution of the sun.*

Solar prominence.   Certain prominences attain a height of as much as 900,000 kilometres, i.e., appreciably more than the distance from the Earth to the Moon.
Mount Wilson photograph.

Subjects for thought.

1. Incorporated in a galaxy (the Milky Way), the sun should not be considered as an isolated celestial body, but as an integral part of a whole, actuated by overall motion.
2. The solar mass is not surrounded by a vacuum but is the centre of an enormous vortex extending beyond the planets and carrying them along in its overall motion.
3. In the centre of the vortex, the sun, swept along in the same overall motion, rotates on its own axis in approximately 25 days.
4. Solar prominences prove that the sun is not an inert mass, but is actuated by internal motion.
5. Solar radiation is striking proof of the sun's evolution.
6. The sun, incorporated in an expanding Universe (as are all the celestial bodies), participates in general expansion.
7. Every mass in rotation is deformed (see Plate 8), flattening at the poles and swelling at the equator until such time as the hump thus formed is expelled.   Actuated by rotary motion, the sun does not attract the planets, as Newton thought, but periodically expels one.

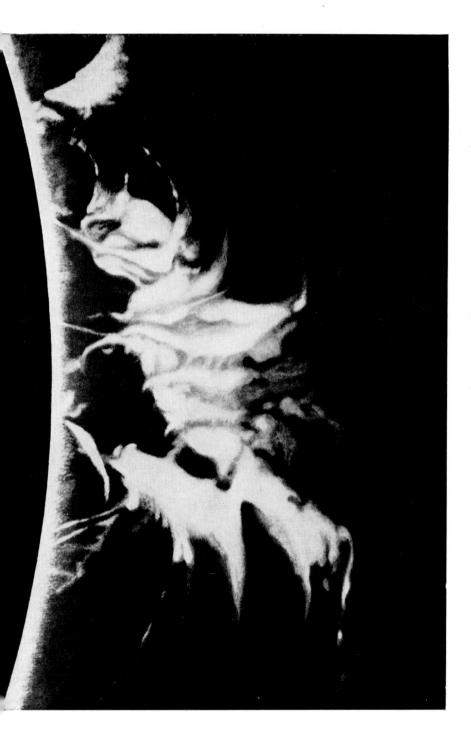

Plate 3 : *Evolution of the planets.*

Although its diameter is eleven times greater than that of the Earth, Jupiter turns on its own axis in less than 10 hours. This rapid rotation produces a visible flattening of the planet and frequent expulsion of satellites. Because of its gaseous condition, Jupiter does not turn in one complete block but rotates more rapidly at the equator than at the poles.

Photograph of Jupiter by Rudaux and Vaucouleurs. From "L'Astronomie". (Larousse.)

Subjects for thought.

1. Incorporated in the solar system, the planets participate in its evolution just as the sun, incorporated in a galaxy, participates in galactic evolution.
2. This participation in universal evolution affects the planets in the same way as the galaxies, that is, by general expansion.
3. Expansion in the planets is manifested by the progressive increase in the distance that separates them from the sun, by the expansion of their constituent elements, and by their periodic expulsion of satellites once they are actuated by a motion of rotation.
4. Jupiter's flattening process and lack of cohesion prove that the celestial bodies, far from being stable, evolve continuously.

Legend in the plate : The Earth.

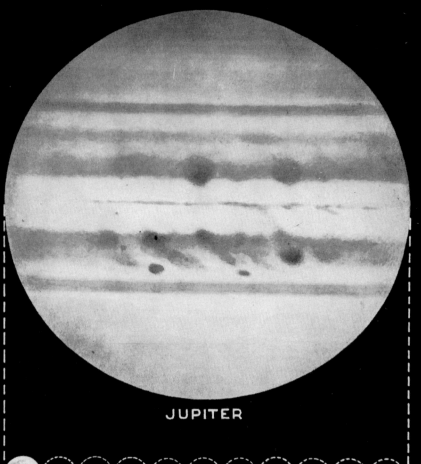

JUPITER

TERRE

Plate 4 : *Evolution of the comets.*

Evolution of the celestial bodies is particularly spectacular in the case of the comets, whose tails, spread out in space, sometimes exceed in length the distance that separates the Earth from the sun (approximately 150 million kms) : for example, the Great Comet of 1843 (reproduced opposite) was not less than 320 million kms. in length.

Photograph from "L'Astronomie" by Rudaux and Vaucouleurs. (Larousse.)

The comet tail does not follow the direction of motion of the nucleus but is thrust away from the sun, as shown in the bottom figure. This thrust is a clear indication of centrifugal force inside the solar vortex.

Also from "L'Astronomie" by Rudaux and Vaucouleurs.

Subjects for thought.

1. Where do the comets come from ?
2. Why is their disintegration so much more marked than that of the planets ?
3. Why do they have a much more eccentric orbit than that of the planets ?
4. Is not the thrust away from the sun that is brought to bear on comet tails a proof that universal gravitation does not exist ? (These questions were studied in Chapter Five, Section 6.)

Legend in the plate : Perihelion.

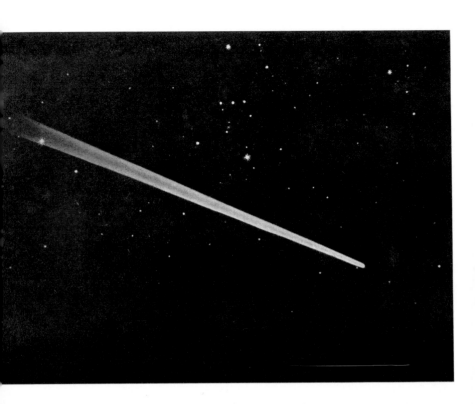

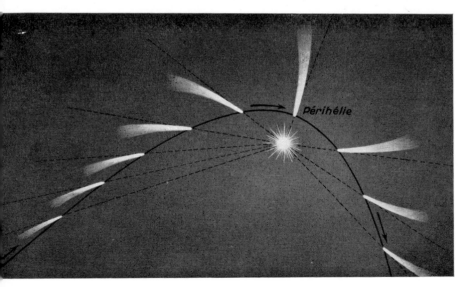

Périhélie

Plate 5 : *Evolution of matter.*

The explosion of an atomic bomb is one of the most striking demonstrations of universal evolution in the heart of matter. The phenomenon of radioactivity on which it is based consists of a spontaneous disintegration of the radioactive bodies. This signifies that evolution extends from the infinitesimally small to the infinitely large and that all its facets are interdependent.

Subjects for thought.

1. The phenomenon of radioactivity can only be explained if it is accepted that the intrinsic nature of the elementary particle of the Universe is motion.
2. It indicates that these elementary particles in motion are subject to universal evolution, manifesting itself by a general expansion of all particles. This expansion causes the most complex bodies to explode and emit alpha, beta and gamma particles.
3. The phenomenon of radioactivity makes it possible to understand what happens in all (and not only radioactive) bodies. The less complex ones are composed of elementary particles in motion just as are their more complex counterparts.
(Photograph from the Viollet Collection.)

Plate 6 : *Evolution of life and thought.*

Evolution is generalized and permeates not only matter but also life and thought. The diplodocus (above) is the largest and most famous of the dinosaurs of the Secondary era ; he disappeared suddenly at the dawn of the Tertiary. As to the skull of the Chapelle-aux-Saints (below) exhibited in the Musée de l'Homme, it still has generally simian features : a flattened cranium and large supra-orbital arches.

Reproduced from "Les hommes fossiles" by Boule and Vallois.

Subjects for thought.

1. Is not the life of the individual—birth, growth, ageing and death—unquestionable proof that evolution is the fundamental phenomenon of life ?
2. Does not evolution of the species imply general evolution in the conditions on the surface of this planet ?
3. Evolution of thought develops parallel with cerebral evolution. Life and thought are therefore intimately linked.

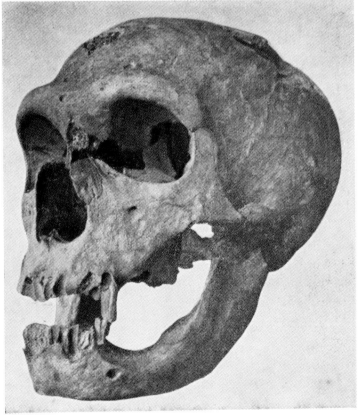

Plate 7 : *The elementary particle and its movement.*

As the elementary particles consist of motion, they all exert pressure on each other. Subjected from all sides to equal pressures, they assume a spherical form (Fig. 1).

But inside this sphere, movement, which cannot be spherical, becomes rotary; as a consequence the sphere is deformed, becoming flattened at the poles and swelling at the equator (Fig. 2).

This discrepancy between internal movement and external pressure is responsible for the evolution of the elementary particle which, in its turn, is the cause of general evolution of the Universe.

Two particles in contact at their equators transmit to each other their movements which cancel each other out in the same way as two saw-toothed wheels in gear. When in contact, such wheels cannot avoid equalizing their movements (Fig. 3).

In vortex movement, the central particles are subject to greater pressure than those at the periphery and their respective diameters are consequently different. The equalizing movements accordingly are effected in the same way as those between two saw-toothed wheels of different diameters, the smaller turning faster than the larger (Fig. 4).

Subjects for thought.

1. What is motion ?
2. What is matter ?
3. What is the relation between matter and motion ?

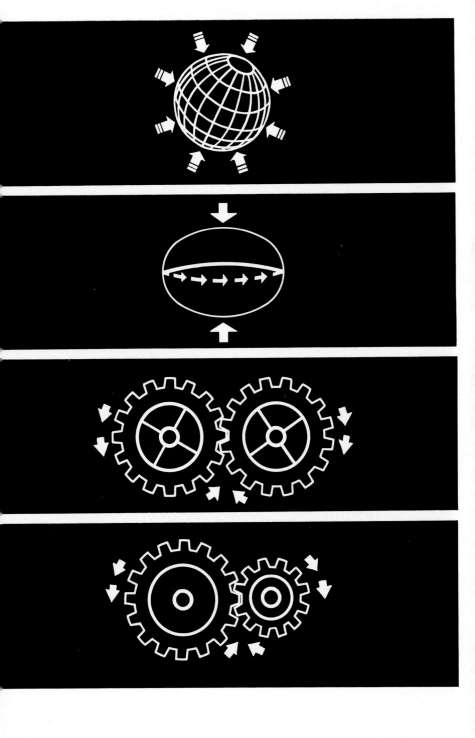

Plate 8 : *Progressive deformation of a rotating mass.*

When a mass rotates in a less dense medium, its progressive deformation, which is due to the lack of sufficient resistance in the surrounding medium, leads to the expulsion of fragments.

This is a general phenomenon and occurs at all levels of the Universe. It can be observed not only at galactic level (see M 51 of the Hunting Dogs : Plate 1), but also at lower scales as it is the cause of the expulsion of planets by the sun and of satellites by the planets.

Subjects for thought.

1. The celestial bodies are masses subject to the general laws of universal dynamics.
2. The Newtonian Theory on the attraction of the planets by the sun is contrary to all tests which show that a rotating mass expels but particles does not attract them.
3. Deformation of a mass as the result of rotation is unquestionable : for example, in Jupiter, the flattening process is clearly visible. The Earth too is flattened and its diameter measures 43 kms more at the equator than between the poles.
4. The expansion of the celestial bodies at their equators and the expulsion of parts of their mass is in keeping with the general expansion of the Universe.

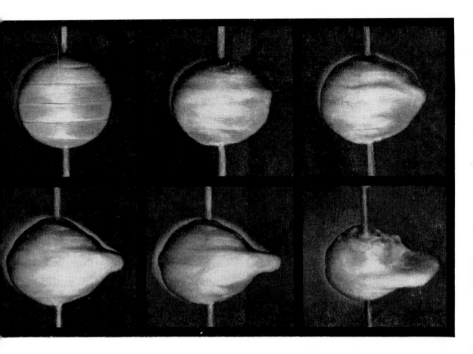
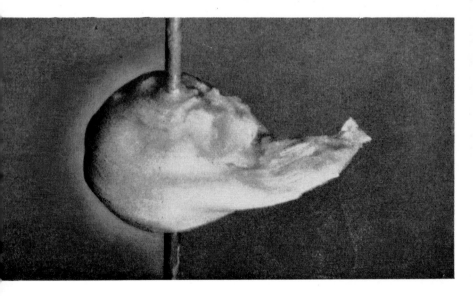

Plate 9 : *The Earth's orbit lengthens with each revolution.*

General expansion of the Universe results not only in an increase in the distance between the centres of galaxies (Hubble's law) but, inside each galaxy, in an increase in the distance between the celestial bodies.   The planets consequently move further away from the sun each year.

Proof of orbital lengthening is supplied by the shift in the Earth's aphelion (the point furthest removed from the sun) which is never at the same position of the orbit but advances from year to year in the direction of the Earth's movement.

This shift in the aphelion is unquestionable proof of evolution in the solar system.

Another proof of increase in orbit length is supplied by Bode's law (Chapter Five, Section 4).

Subject for thought.

In a Universe in general expansion, is it possible that a minute system like the solar system would constitute an exception to the general rule, that its celestial bodies would always describe the same orbits, and that it alone would be governed by conditions of permanency while everything else would evolve?

Legends in the plate : Planet's orbit.   Translation force.   Centrifugal force.   Resultant.

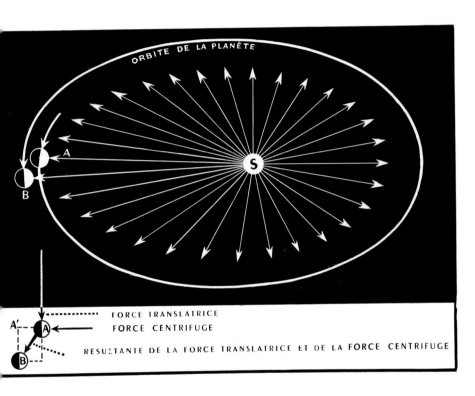

ORBITE DE LA PLANÈTE

S

A

B

FORCE TRANSLATRICE

FORCE CENTRIFUGE

RESULTANTE DE LA FORCE TRANSLATRICE ET DE LA FORCE CENTRIFUGE

A'

A

B

Plate 10: *Unquestionable documentary proof of slow rotation of the Earth in early eras.*

The geologic strata formed during the period of great light are paler than those formed during the period of darkness. This photograph of Syltoppene terrain in Greenland warrants long scrutiny and meditation.

From "La Riviera polaire" by E. Hofer. (Kümmerly and Frey, Berne.)

After having been expelled by the sun, the Earth revolved around it showing always the same face, as is the carse with Mercury at the present moment. Then it started very slowly to rotate on its own axis, one rotation lasting millenia. The succession of long periods of light followed by long periods of darkness is particularly noticeable in this photograph.

Other phenomena, such as the successive glaciation periods, climatic conditions altogether different from those obtaining at the present day, etc., are proof of this slow rotation, but no illustration is as vivid as this photograph. The variations that can be seen inside the strata were caused by changes in light intensity during one translation as a result of the inclination of the Earth's axis.

Subjects for thought.

1. Why does the Earth turn on its own axis?
2. Why have the conditions favoring rotation evolved? (Chapters Five and Six.)

Plate 11 : *Coal deposits are rich in information.*

Repetition of seams in a coal basin.

The beds of coal with their walls and roofs are superimposed a large number of times (400 in the Franco-Belgian basin), thus testifying unquestionably to the seasonal periodicity of the phenomenon.

This can only be satisfactorily explained if the conditions existing in the regions on the borders between the areas of light and darkness at the time of the Earth's slow rotation are understood. As a result of the inclination of the Earth's axis, these regions passed alternately from light to darkness in the course of one translation of the Earth around the sun ; the formation of coal beds therefore offers invaluable material from which to calculate the age of the Earth (Chapter Six, Section 11).

Subjects for thought.

1. What were the conditions of life on the Earth during the period of slow rotation ?
2. In particular, what were the conditions of life in the borderline areas between light and darkness ?

Legends in the plate : Roof. Upright trunk. Coal. Wall.

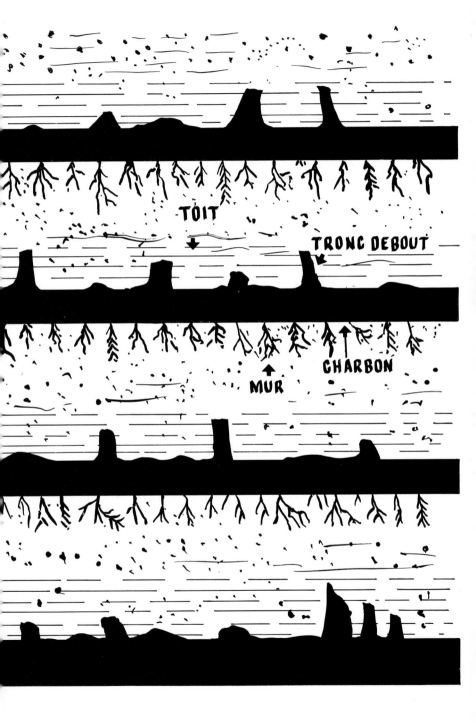

Plate 12: *Dislocation of continents according to Alfred Wegener,* "La Genèse des Continents", (Librairie Nizet, Paris).

The periodic expulsion of planets by the sun and of satellites by the planets is one of the most important effects of universal expansion on the celestial bodies of the solar system.

The expulsion of the moon by the Earth having created a pit in the area of the Pacific, the continents were drawn towards this depression—Asia, Europe and Africa in an eastward direction and America, at that time forming part of Europe and Africa, to the westward. These two tractions in opposite directions resulted, at the end of the Secondary era, in the dislocation of the continents, as represented by Wegener, and in the great fracture that widened progressively, as the two continental shelves drew away from each other, to become the Atlantic Ocean.

Subjects for thought.

1. The shifting of the continents, quite inexplicable in a permanent world, becomes perfectly comprehensible in the context of universal evolution.
2. The phenomenon of the moon's expulsion explains why the continents, which had not moved in relation to each other before the Secondary era, suddenly began to drift.

Legends in the plate: Upper Carboniferous. Eocene. Lower Quaternary.

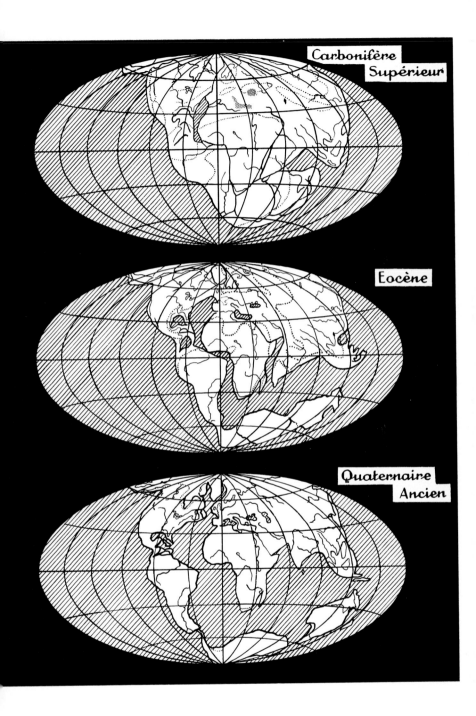

Carbonifère Supérieur

Eocène

Quaternaire Ancien

Plate 13 : *Chart of continental movements.*

The direction of displacement, shown by arrows, clearly indicates the traction towards the Pacific pit.

According to Taylor. "Bull. Geol. Soc. of America". T 21, June 1910.

The continental shift generally resulted in the formation of chains of mountains in the prow of the moving areas.

The events shown in this and the previous plate can only be understood when it is realized that they are the result of the expulsion of the moon, that is, of the continent of Gondwana, which was formerly in the Pacific area.

Subjects for thought.

1. The continents, stable up to the end of the Secondary era, suddenly began to shift in the region of the Pacific. Why?
2. Numerous geologists admit, on the basis of Suess' work, that a large continent existed, at least up to the end of the Triassic period, in the Pacific area. It is no longer there. What has happened to it?
3. When it is realized that all celestial bodies evolve, is there any justification for believing that the Earth is an exception to the rule and never changes?

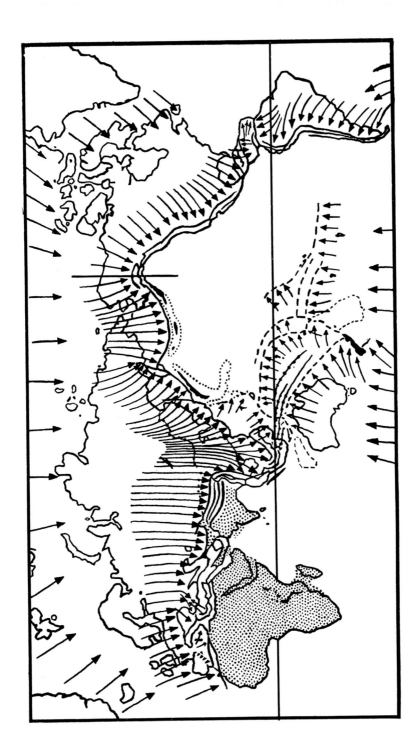

Page 14 : *Subterranean earthquakes and ocean deeps of the Pacific.*

The position of the graded series of subterranean earthquakes is indicated by the hachures, that of the ocean deeps by the dotted lines. As is seen by the crown of seismic centres surrounding the Pacific, the continents have still not altogether settled in their new places.

According to Goguel. "Traité de tectonique", (Masson.)

The arrangement of the seismic centres in the Pacific is quite different from that in the Atlantic. In the latter, there are admittedly certain centres along the coasts (the disasters of Lisbon, Agadir, etc.), but the most numerous and important are to be found the full length of the ridge that separates the Atlantic bed in two in the form of a large "S" and probably coincides with the point at which the two Americas, on the one hand, and Europe and Africa, on the other, separated from each other and began to drift, the former towards the west and the latter towards the east.

Subjects for thought.

1. Do not the fundamental differences between the positions of the seismic centres in the Atlantic and the Pacific correspond to the different conditions brought about by the shift of the continents?

2. Are not seismic centres a proof that the surface of the globe is in a process of continuous evolution?

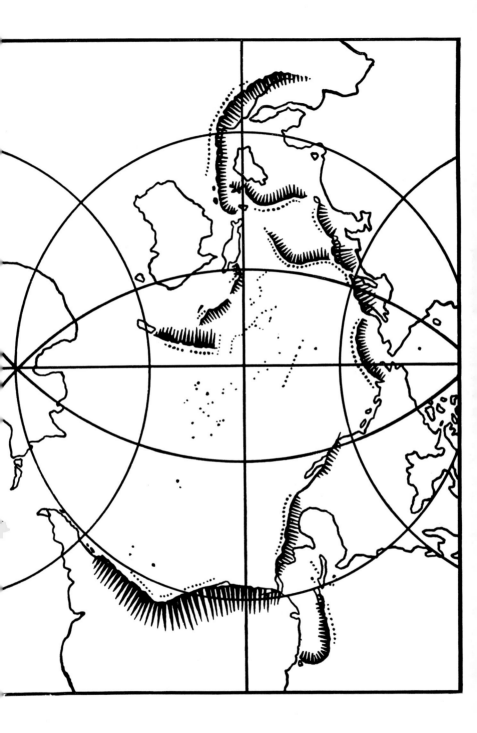

Plate 15: *Fate of the Earth and of all the planets* (or Sir James Jeans' cigar).

This cigar clearly indicates the different stages through which the planets pass. After having been expelled by the sun, the planets, compressed by the surrounding medium which is very dense in the centre of the vortex, are also dense and small. They move around the sun without rotating, showing always the same face. Mercury and Venus are at present at this stage. The further they move away from the sun, the less are they compressed by the ambient medium; they accordingly increase in volume, begin to rotate on their own axis and then expel satellites. The Earth has one, Mars two. The Asteroids, which come next, are probably formed by the debris of a planet. Jupiter, further removed and much less compressed by the vortex medium, has become enormous and essentially gaseous. It rotates extremely rapidly and has expelled numerous satellites. Saturn, still further removed, is very similar to Jupiter; it is also gaseous and has a ring, in addition to numerous satellites.

The expulsion of satellites continually reduces a planet's mass and beyond the point at which Jupiter is situated at present, its diameter begins to decrease. As the planetary vortex's cohesion becomes increasingly attenuated, its peripheral satellites are gradually swept away. This is the case with Uranus, which now has only four. Decay is rapid. Neptune's volume is still further reduced. It has only one satellite, while Pluto appears to have none at all. The latter is now reduced to a tiny nucleus.

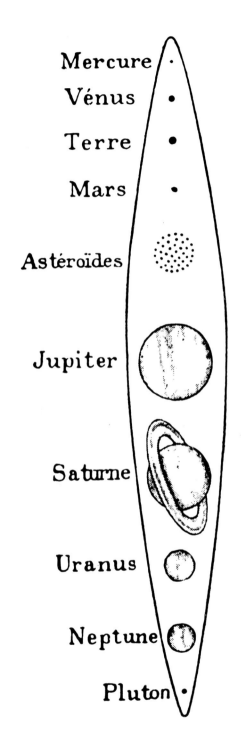

Mercure

Vénus

Terre

Mars

Astéroïdes

Jupiter

Saturne

Uranus

Neptune

Pluton

Subjects for thought.

1. Evolution is continuous and of all time. It is not limited to the past but continues in the present and will continue in the future.

2. Evolution is all-pervading and influences all celestial bodies. As soon as these have been created and constitute separate entities, they pass through various stages of growth. They then enter into a process of decay that finally leads to their total disintegration.

3. The Earth is subject to universal evolution and its fate is no different from that of the other planets.

Legends in the plate: Mercury. Venus. The Earth. Mars. The Asteroids. Jupiter. Saturn. Uranus. Neptune. Pluto.

SET IN MONOTYPE TIMES
MANUFACTURED BY IMPRIMERIE CENTRALE S. A.
NEUCHATEL (SWITZERLAND)
PUBLISHED BY LES ÉDITIONS DU MONT-BLANC
GENEVA (SWITZERLAND)

DATE DUE

GAYLORD			PRINTED IN U.S.A